DAVID ORMSBEE has also written

THE SOUND OF AN AMERICAN

"David Ormsbee . . . is a writer of both tremendous power and sensitivity. In *The Sound of an American* he has written something out of his own flesh and bones—used his life blood as ink—something which so cried out to him to be written that it sounds as if it had written itself. . . . It is modern. It is sensitive, sometimes startlingly so. It is tough, it is cruel, it is bitter. And it is tremendously real."

FANNY BUTCHER, *The Chicago Tribune*

"The war novel I have been waiting to read. . . . It is the most forthright, hard-hitting, square-jawed story of the Second World War I have yet encountered."

DAVID H. APPEL, *The Cleveland News*

"David Ormsbee is a born story-teller and writes with a massive vigor that carries the reader along from first page to last. . . . The war scenes in this book are among the starkest and most gripping in the English language. . . . The love story has its tender and its terrible moments."

ALEXANDER KENDRICK, *Philadelphia Inquirer*

"The blunt, brutal immediacy of impact of the war material, and the speed, suspense and excitement of its plot, are what make this book the engrossing entertainment it is."

ORVILLE PRESCOTT, *The New York Times*

Published by

E. P. DUTTON & CO., INC.

CHICO GOES TO THE WARS

CHICO

Goes to the Wars

A CHRONICLE ... 1933-1943

BY

David Ormsbee

*And some there be, which have no
memorial; who are perished, as though
they had never been; and are become
as though they had never been born;
and their children after them.*

ECCLESIASTICUS XLIV

A. S. BARNES & COMPANY

NEW YORK

AMERICAN BOOK–STRATFORD PRESS, INC., NEW YORK

FOR MY SON

This book is based on private journals and sketch books that have not been published before except part of Book One which appeared in *Esquire* and part of Book Five which appeared in *Cosmopolitan*.

CONTENTS

LIST OF ILLUSTRATIONS

A FOREWORD ON CHICO HIMSELF

There's not a roaring blade in all this town
Can go so far towards Hell for half-a-crown
As I for sixpence, for *I* know the way . . .
"Tartufe's" epilogue

We are broad natures . . . capable of accommodating
every possible contradiction and of contemplating simul-
taneously the two infinities, the infinite above us, the
infinite of lofty ideals, and the infinite below, the infinite
of the lowest and most repulsive degradation . . . we find
room for everything, we reconcile ourselves to everything . . .

Dostoevski

THIS book was put together because there was still missing
a book on the unimportant people who fight the wars and
whom the experts ignore; the little people whom the casu-
alty lists only put down in round numbers. The camera can
not manage to catch them sharply for they are the blurred
faces behind the strutting leaders, they are the running
shapes dodging the tanks, they are little factory clogs bolting
together engines, they are the voices standing in line,
memories of rotting hay that once talked, laughed, forni-
cated. . . . The cameras, the press services seem to miss them.
Sometimes of course somebody dusts off capital letters and

says fine things about the Little People, the Have-nots, Common Men . . . but you can't really see them as they are in such fine capital type dress . . .

II

"There are only the rich and the poor, the hunters and the hunted, and the living and the dead," Chico's notebook says. Let me explain this fellow Chico.

This book, unlike the novels I write as a trade, is not a work of fiction. It is a picture of places, people, armies and wars— wars between the year nineteen thirty-three and the year nineteen forty-three; the man who sees these wars, these cities, these people, and who draws the pictures of the people and the soldiers, and the hopes and foulness of mankind, and the heavy purposeless splendor of war, is Chico.

And who is Chico? I am Chico, several friends of mine are Chico, one enemy is Chico; some reporters and writers I knew all over the world are Chico. This is no begging for sophisticated laughter. You see, we were writers and artists, and some of us drank and some of us chased the girls and some of us had ideas and systems and hopes, and a few of us had hates . . . but all of us had to draw and write for a living and so we wrote of wars and low, malicious leaders. And of the little people of Europe, and Asia, and America, in thin pants, and of the boiling madness in Munich beer halls, around English diplomatic tea tables—and after a while we found out what they would print of ours and what they wouldn't. The boundaries of shapes and the scales of the reptile were not what they wanted from us . . . then.

After all, Wall Street was still in business, and the Flivver King and the ex-Air-Hero had their Nazi crosses (hung like albatrosses around their necks) and it was a fine world and would go on being fine and dividends were a safe twenty

percent. We were to them like ghosts in a pawn shop haunt-
ing our overcoats . . .

III

All right, we didn't mind—that is, most of us didn't mind
—but we *had* to write about a lot of things the news services
didn't want. So when we heard something, saw something
that couldn't go over the proud Associated Press wires, or
be printed in the *New York Times* (General Franco gave a
banquet to *some* American reporters when Madrid fell) or
be as safe as the pap—the stuff "experts" turned out—we
let Chico write it.

And Chico wrote it for years . . . and sometimes he wrote
it as fiction for the slick magazines, and some of it went
into news-letters, and most into private journals and after
a while Chico became the man who knew a lot of things;

things wrung, depleted, devoured unprofitably—about the little people who marched and sweated and starved to build guns, and about armies, and double-crossing in Oxford accents, and Moors cutting Christian throats with the full approval of the Bishop; and this book is the story of Chico's wars, and what he saw and what he said and what he drew. This is no Faustian fever brewed on mere words at a New York literary tea—Chico was always a lug . . .

So Chico served us cowardly mice well. He took all the raps. Now, one thing I must make clear—none of us who made up Chico were "military experts"—the kind you hear blabber on the radios, or who go knocking down battles for three cents on newsstands. None of us was a hand-made, home-grown "military strategist" recruited from weird adventure pulp magazines. "You can't accumulate eternity with a few well-turned words," Chico once said.

IV

Nothing in this book will help win the war or end wars forever. Nothing here will amaze a general staff or dictate a new form of warfare. There are no "groups" or "causes" here. But this is how wars happen, what they do, how people take them, how children and pregnant women die, how soldiers of master races are hashed into dead heroes, how the little people, those who just stand and wait for orders, live today in the tangled mess of a tattered civilization. "Pity is a naked thing shivering in public," Chico said and never asked for pity.

I suppose there is plenty of humor in his book. That may shock a lot of people. Perhaps there is too much drinking and love-making and too much about the soul, and blood and death and fun under fire, and the shape of women's bodies, and the decay in the minds of shouting insane leaders right off the devil's spit. But that's the way things were, the way things are. Chico never approved of leering appraisals or acquiescent shrugs. He loved people.

This is your world, my world, Chico's world—with no idea of the shape of things to come.

Anyway you can't sit there and blame me for it. Blame Chico. He saw it this way, drew the pictures and said this is how I went to the wars; I laughed, cried, sang and had my entrails and sinews in agony.

What did he look like, this Chico? Where did he come from? Funny, I can't remember. I can see him drinking beer in a dive in Rome . . . drinking *bocks* . . . and saying . . .

> Men must endure
> Their going hence,
> Even as their coming hither,
> Ripeness is all . . .

Lots of people say Chico wrote that. Taking the rap for someone, I suppose, as usual—someone who needed a Chico to blame . . .

V

The last time some of us saw Chico was in France, in a village near Dijon, and he was walking up and down the street, a scarf knotted cravat-fashion around his throat, smoking one cigarette after another, and he had just come back from watching Frenchmen (whom Pétain and Laval had picked out and handed over to the Germans) shot as hostages. Hostages for what? asked Chico of the faces swarming past and he went on pacing back and forth smoking cigarettes. . . .

I think you know now about Chico and why this is his book and why it isn't fiction—or made up—and can't have the deft, swift satisfied finality of the "experts."

VI

Sitting one noon in a California restaurant with William Faulkner, and listening to talk about a motion picture that would lack glamour, I knew suddenly I was going to do this book, and while William Faulkner nodded and the hard sunshine, stiff as yellow tin, flooded the sidewalk near the open door, I wished for Chico again, because he had a way of making a gathering of two or three writers sound like a convention . . .

And now the book is done and in your hands—a book without glamour. . . .

DAVID ORMSBEE

Vienna 1933—*New York City* 1943

Book One

THE CAGE OF EUROPE

Chapter 1

VIENNA

He was *sitting drinking Rhine wine-and-seltzer in a little café under the crest of the* Kaiserschritzen *regiment and the red-coated man was playing one of those over-sweet low Strauss waltzes with much* Schlämperei *when suddenly there was gunfire—not just machine guns . . . but the heavy bark of field artillery. Chico turned to the waiter who stood starchily formidable at his elbow.*

"Did you hear it?"

The waiter, an old man with war medals and two fingers missing on his right hand was crying, big heavy tears scarring his paper-gray face.

"I hear . . . it's the dwarfed rat Dollfuss and the clericals and the Heimwehr shelling the workers' apartment houses apart. My house, too . . . "

The waltz sounded very sour and the hideous solid shelling went on and that was how Chico came to go to Vienna, to his first war . . .

SHORTY THE KILLER

I don't remember why I had come to Vienna but I stayed two years . . . and I don't remember knowing anything about the politics of the damned sad city about to be murdered

by the dressy, warped little midget, *Der kleiderständer* . . .
but him I did know.

He was always entertaining newspaper men and saying
bright things and he looked like a small rat tossed out by
the better class rat people, and now he lived among men
hunting a hole of his own to boss. He was silly and very

vain. One of the café stories about him was that when he
went any place he didn't take a train—he sent himself air-
mail. But he was a killer and wanted to create a little fascist
world as big as himself, and he prayed a lot and went to
Mass and the morning after the murder of the women and
children in the apartment houses, I saw him in a church
and he was looking at his midget hands locked in tiny
prayer, and, I think it was a trick of the altar lighting, but
they looked red, as if covered with blood. And next door
the small Hungarian band played *tziganer* music. All that
night there was shooting. . . .

DEATH OF A CITY

The street rabble was up early that morning. They went
to Mass and looked at their Jewish God on the cross, and
then went and threw stones at the synagogue in the Seiten-
stattengasse in the mistaken idea, I suppose, that you only
have to respect one dead Jew nailed to a cross.

II

It's very confusing, this Vienna, because you can't believe
your eyes and ears, as you see the clerical dictatorship in
action and you wonder what this priests' fascism will lead to.
The Nazis don't want it. They have been gathering at
the German Embassy in the Metternichstrasse singing and
shouting . . . *"Sieg Heil, Sieg Heil, ein Volk, ein Reich, ein
Fuehrer!"* . . . and the police have just been standing around
and winking and nodding as if to say . . . break it up, boys
. . . break it up . . . you'll have your day, too . . .
About the only thing to do is to sit in the Schwarzenberg
Café and count the broken heads passing . . . each head held
carefully in its owner's dirty bloody hands. The Berlin radio
is active and the *Reichs Rundfunk Gesellschaft* is giving us
Putzi Hanfstangl, the sort of thing Harvard turns out for
Europe or consumes at home as bond salesmen . . .
The copies of the *Deutsche Wehr* are full of skiing pictures and the Franconian wine is not bad . . . but I wish I
could get away. A tall, dark man with a turfed mustache
sits down and bows and I bow back. He is a French reporter
and he tells me of the hell of a hot time he had when Hearst
visited Hitler and the gay doings at his suite at Bad Nau-
heim. The radio plays the Balenweiler March and the voice
of the repulsive Messiah comes in over the air waves.

They have found a little Jew drinking coffee at the Drei
Husaren and the plate glass windows are falling into shards.
An old hag, roped in holy beads and wearing a hooked cross
arm band passes, shouting:
"Ja oder Nein!!!"

III

Death walked the streets for four days and I saw the stiff
dead rags that were thousands of women, children and
working stiffs beaten to death by the little dwarf. They were
hanging democrats and liberals and socialists, too. I counted
nine. And there was one poor boy so badly broken by bullets
that the police hung him seated in an easy chair.

Of course this was my first war and I was a little soft, but
the man from the London *Times* just smoked his cigarette
and told me about a girl he had. She was very nice—of
typical Viennese quaintness—and had red hair and didn't
drink much, and then we went to the Goethe Hof, once one
of the finest blocks of workers' apartment houses in the
world. It was broken up by shellfire and the dead women
and children lay around on the sidewalks and among the
brick dust.

Toys, books, baby buggies and the remains of meals lay
there, and the police were beating young girls to get them
to tell them where they had hidden their machine guns,
tanks and battleships. Pictures of Christ hung on the burst-
open rooms and a tall lout in a coal scuttle helmet was kicking some Crucifixion pictures and broken bricks into the
face of a dead man, with placid stupidity, or maybe he
brooded on man's brevity or anguish.

All the next week they killed men in the streets because
they wore ragged clothing and had hard, work-horned hands
and I sat in the café wishing I could get my visa and go

home . . . but of course I couldn't get it. My waiter didn't
weep any more. He just stood in baffled frustration emptying
ash trays . . .

"Why should I cry?" he said. "My wife was very old and
always sick."

"It's too bad."

"It's better they killed her. She or I were never *gescheit*."

"And your son?"

"Oh, they'll hang him. They caught him, you know."

"I didn't know."

"Yes. Runt Dollfuss is very firm about hanging tall young
boys . . ."

I shivered. "How can you take it?"

He looked at me, and then at a group of hard, lumpy,
pimply young men with dirty necks in soiled horsehide
jackets. "I've been through a lot. I have no need for a *Klage-
mauer*—a Wailing Wall. See those men?"

"What are they, pimps?"

"Nazis, too. . . . You wait . . . *just* wait . . ."

"For what?"

He didn't answer but gave me a sly conspiratorial look and I went to my room and wrote a short story about a pure, noble girl who was in love with her rich millionaire boss and how it all came out all right when he caught her one day behind the multigraphing machine in the office and improved the specious present ideals she had. I mailed it to New York and I got down a volume of poetry and began to read. They were still shooting near the German Athletic Club on Siebensterngasse and I wanted to get away to frosty pine clearings, and a moon low enough to bite at. Planes passed overhead . . .

> *Kennst du das Haus auf Saulen ruht sein Dach,*
> *Es glanzt der Saal, es schimmert das Gemach,*
> *Und Marmorbilder stehn und sehn mich an:*
> *Was hat man dir, du armes Kind, getan?*
> *Dahin! Dahin*
> *. . . Geht unser Weg; O Vater, lass uns ziehn!*

IV

Every day you could see the Viennese *Deutschmeister* regiment of society people looking like something out of Metro-Goldwyn-Mayer on the streets, and the mad Major Fey leading them, and the jails were very full and you could always find the fat peasant boys in their private group uniforms moving in mobs to beat up workers and small shopkeepers—and the priests were very busy, I remember, running with the holy oils and ashes to mark on brows marked for death . . . *Laudetur Jesus Christus in aeternum amen* . . . The gilt crosses always banging their knees. At night you

could hear women laughing, or crying, and a lot of American
college girls dated the Nazis, I remember, and said to me:
"Isn't it *all* thrilling . . ."

"Yes. Like Typhoid Mary."

V

Then somebody called me on the phone one day and
said come on over to the palace and watch the Dwarf die, and
I never found out who called . . . but the police were on the
streets and private armies, too, and it seems the little monster
who lived by murder had just been murdered himself. By
bigger killers, sent by Hitler—and left to bleed to death on
a yellow sofa at the Bundeskanzleramt, the old Metternich
palace. He had a little hole shot in his neck but they didn't
get a doctor, and didn't get him a priest, and so he bled to
death. There was not much blood in him and he died with-

out the last rites and he went to hell (as he had a right to expect).

After a while they caught the killers by saying they had safe conducts to the German border but of course they didn't, and later they hung nine of them. It was all mixed up to a poor American *dummkopf* like myself.

It was the most confused war I ever saw—but you see it was our first on the spot since my grandfather chased Comanches. Later, as you shall read in this book, I became very expert at telling about wars and I never became confused or annoyed at death. Not too much. But my first war was badly muddled and what I wrote about it was badly done, because of a tedious conscience full of decencies, and reticences about murder.

I saw the body of the dreadful midget and I attended the high Holy Mass they gave him. They hid him away under heavy marble in a stink of rotting roses, so he couldn't get out, I suppose, and now he is in hell, as he never got to a priest in time.

Prince von Stahremberg was in his best uniform and big with a sense of expectancy at the Mass.

The next time I saw Prince Ernst Rudiger von Stahremberg he was drunk and had a dancer on his arm . . . but I got out of him the idea that he was going to defy Hitler and run Austria as his personal hunting preserve and didn't I think the dancer had fine thighs . . . The next time after that I saw him, he was sweating very hard in a very fine restaurant and Franz von Papen was biting off words and spitting them into his ear; and I left long before Hitler marched in shouting *"Anschluss!"* as if he were playing a kids' game and *Mittel Europa* was to fall to him as if he were calling "Red Rover, Red Rover, would you come over" . . .

VI

On the train taking me to Italy there was a reporter from the *Deutsches Nachrichten Buro,* the official Nazi news service . . .

"Glad to get away?" he asked me.

"Yes. It's too confusing."

"It will get more confusing," he said with a phlegmy cough.

"Well, I'm an American. It's nothing to me . . . or us."

He smiled and we went to the Wagon Lit diner and we drank a fair wine and worse coffee. A girl sat near us, her tears delicately salting the apéritif set before her.

"You know . . . *Der Fuehrer* is a great man. He figured America out just right," said the Nazi reporter.

"How?" I made a drawing of Hitler as a satyr.

"He wants you to go on saying it's nothing to you—for a long time. It's part of the *Fuehrer Prinzip.*"

"Why?"

"By that time the world will be a German world . . . a *'National Sozialistiche Deutsche Arbeiter Partei'* world!"

I laughed. "That's only a marching song. *'Today we rule Germany, tomorrow we own the world'* . . . Not a good marching song, either."

He smiled again and nodded. *"Wunderbar.* How well Der Fuehrer knows you. We mean the *Horst Wessel Lied.* We mean everything we say. This is *our* era—*our* times. You will only wake up yelling *hilfe, hilfe,* when it is too late."

"Let's have another bottle of wine," I said. "You're *so* wrong."

"Sie irren Sich," he said very low, and then we were at the border and a storm trooper danced on my luggage and asked me the shape of my grandfather's nose and other trivia. I had some notes they wanted to take from me but the reporter said:

"Nichts unternehmen! Respect the Americans!"

And I thanked him and he said: "See you in Washington in 1944. My uncle shall be the first American *gauleiter* . . ."

He was mad as a hatter, I wrote in my journals. But as I've said before, I was very new to war and this was my first one, and Lindbergh and Henry Ford were to wear their Nazi crosses proud around their necks. And I wanted to write polite magazine fiction that year . . .

ROME

In a way, Chico's friends said later, it was a shame he didn't go to Abyssinia and cover the Ethiopian War. It spoiled his perfect record. He couldn't say to his grand-

*children that he had covered every War II of the White
and the Black and the Yellow Peoples.*

*He was at the Sistine Chapel most of the time studying
the great ceiling, and sketching and writing, and he lived in
a dust heap behind the Arch near the Borghese Gardens.
When Mussolini sent his grape-growers and alley-singers
and bombing planes into Abyssinia, Chico's landlord, a fat,
happy wop with three stomachs in layers under his midriff
and a lover of* capri bianca, *said:*

*"We are hungry for land. He says we are prolific and we
intend to stay so."*

"Who says?" asked Chico.

"Him. The strutting one at the Palazzo Venezia."

"Where is Abyssinia?"

*The landlord rolled his eyes and spit on his unclean floor.
"Devil take it. You think I ever want to settle there!* Ming!"

THE ARTISTS' LIFE

They were shouting in the streets before the *Via Imperiale*
monument in the morning. *To whom belongs victory* said
the radio and the mouths said *A Noi!* (to us) and that made
them happy and they went along the streets as if a war was
fun. They were stirred up to almost a cruel perversity . . .

I had shaved and put on my best suit and I wondered if I
should cut my hair. A great art critic had invited me to
dinner, and he would say wonderful things about my paintings in the hope I would give him several free. I would. I
knew his wife slightly and there would be an American
Motion Picture Actress whose rear view I had always remembered, and an Oil Driller who was going to find lots of oil
for the Duce (I had a hard time getting him to stop saying
the Douche—he was from Texas and carelessly educated at
Yale) . . .

CRITIC IN ROME

Martin, the Art Critic, respected my drawings and even liked me a little. I don't know why he thought I would like an Italian night club, but it was a fine change from the usual entertainment they dig up for painters and writers. I even borrowed a pressed tie.

We rode—the Art Critic, his wife, the Motion Picture Actress, Oil Driller and me—a long time along the river. We drove by old trees dying and growing beards in the process, like old men wilting away. There were even gypsies singing along the river banks just the way they do in motion pictures and in musical comedies. It was pleasant near the Tiber and somewhere lurked Pontassieve and Caprese and Roman history.

II

The music was very low at the Lido roadhouse and a dozen people ran around in a mild state of tango.

There were three kinds of good wine and a local *chianti*. Martin—the Art Critic—had been particular about the sherry. He was old-fashioned enough always to see that the ladies got a good, clear oporto sherry. The waiter with the wide-set eyes of a mystic had served the amontillado with the julienne, and a beaune burgundy went with the great turkey padded with Brussels sprouts and chestnuts. Many people sat around dining at the Lido and I enjoyed myself.

Emma, the Critic's wife, beamed at the Oil Driller who was having trouble with the passionate glances he was receiving. The Motion Picture Actress, amethysts on her ears, was toying with her ices and glaring at Oil Driller who was bent very close to the shiny, silk-covered breasts of Emma, talking very low (you would think they were trying to act out a best seller plot).

Emma was well curved and her taffy colored hair was thick and curly with an uplifted hairdress that exposed her pretty ears. She had a sweet, flexible American Kansas voice and gracious listening personality. She was a highbrow—the understanding kind—with a habit of showing an inch of pink tongue with every smile and rolling her big eyes as if

every statement made to her was of great and grave importance, and something T. S. Eliot or Bernard Shaw would love. It was a finishing school manner—more manner than finish.

Oil Driller whispered on, reckless of consequences. He was the kind of goon *all* women love.

Martin was on his feet nodding to the head waiter who smirked over to us, holding hands with himself, followed by a fat little waiter bearing an iced bucket of *Heidsick* and *strega* bottles.

"Fortunatissimo."

The head waiter bowed, turned triumphantly to the wine bucket.

"Twenty-two. A fine year for champagne."

Martin nodded. "Open it."

"Si, eccellenza."

"Really," said Emma, looking over the high-ceilinged room, "champagne always makes me feel like a battleship launching."

"Battleship launchings?" Oil Driller smiled, his tanned face very handsome over his white tie and shirt. "Not *that*."

(The truth is people do not, I thought, talk like Noel Coward even in Italian night clubs. Oil Driller thought his "Not *that*," very bright dialogue).

Martin lifted high a glass of the light, bubbling wine and I stopped gnawing on *bel paese* cheese.

The Actress watched the wine waiter, competent as a Jesuit, fill her glass. "Bubble bubble boil. Get to the point, Martin, I'm dying of thirst."

Emma gripped Martin's hand and they all looked at him. He bent in a small bow and made a plausive gesture.

"To Emma. Married five years tonight!"

"That's something!"

"Your health."

"Bottoms up . . ."

We drank. Emma slowly, the Actress her eyes lidded, Oil Driller with the distaste of a hard drinker for this berp-water.

Emma sipped. The bubbles broke. I wet my tongue and never had champagne tasted so full of many things, such platitudes prettily turned. A great cloying comfort seemed to run through me. Let them fight over Oil Driller . . .

III

The wine waiter popped another cork, his face very grave as he wrestled with the bottle neck wrapped in a damp linen, and when the cork banged his features relaxed and he held the bottle high, like a head hunter proud of his trophy. Then he poured swiftly, refilling all the glasses. Oil Driller laid a fat brown palm across his and asked for brandy. The head waiter stood by, eyelids down, as if trying politely to stare down his own nostrils. He brought *Asti spumante*.

Emma lifted her glass.

"Really now, who next to toast?"

The Motion Picture Actress pointed her jade cigarette holder at Martin. She had been to Vassar but her press agent was ashamed of the fact and said she was hillbilly.

"Martin. *Heureux comme un roi.*"

"Well," said Oil Driller.

The Actress with no coquettish embellishments lifted her glass toward Martin. *"La bonne aventure, la triste aventure."*

Oil Driller scowled at the Actress.

I said: *"Raide et très audacieuse."*

"Nonsense," said Martin with somber distinction. *"Merci bien."*

"You devil," the Actress said, shaking ash onto the table-cloth. "You know French better than the guide books."

"Only Harvard French."

"Shall we dance?" said Emma, looking at Oil Driller.

Oil Driller set down his glass and took her in his arms. The band droned on its version of *Le Jazz Hot* and The Actress turned to Martin.

Martin said: "I must make a phone call to the American Embassy."

The official radio at the bar said the Italian troops were near Lake Tsana, head of the Blue Nile and England was very angry. They would send a stiff note about it.

IV

At about three o'clock I got tired of touring the night clubs in the Roman night. They were all alike. Small, crowded tables, too many little dark men with hard eyes, too many pretty girls with glazed eyes, too many people who invited you over to their table and left you with the check and a word of cheer. Rich auto kings, Blackshirts in clover. Levantine glitter, over-lithe bodies, credulous, feckless, shallow joy, big blonde bouncing women of forty. Forty is a bad age for hips, said the Motion Picture Actress, thinking of her own age and the eyes of a camera . . .

Martin was beginning to yawn, and the naked cigarette girls couldn't find his brand of cigars. We were at the Cave Door or it may have been at the Double Dante Club. In both places the imported Paris chef was a tradition rather than a habit and none of the wine came in the right kind of bottles. Dancers nude and feathered from American vaudeville fought strenuously against *le hot* music and lost the battle in an odor of grease paint . . .

Everyone agreed it was time to say good-night. Emma and the Actress were working with powder puffs and lipstick on their faces. We men were rolling poker dice at the bar with a Polski Count from Warsaw—all except Martin, who was at the cloak racks hunting a phone to check on the American Embassy.

The Actress wrapped her great white coat around her body as if it were a cape out of an historical pageant. She spoke softly and coolly but the full disk of her pupils blazed and the scythe of her smile hung crooked.

"I've had a hell of an evening. Just lovely."

Emma took Oil Driller in her arms.

"One last dance."

Emma and Oil Driller danced as though they were going to be flayed alive in five minutes with dull knives and the last waiter read *Popolo d'Italia* and picked his nose.

"Emma is a dancing fool," I said.

The Actress smiled, her mouth thin and red like a slit throat. "It would be *so* cheap to say that the last word of your statement is true."

Martin came back to join us.

The Actress looked into the impenetrable dark of his eyes.

"Emma looks wonderful tonight, doesn't she, Martin? I don't see how any man can resist her, do you?"

It was a very strong cigar and Martin coughed slightly as he sucked in the scented smoke. The band played softer—an Italian street song—a milder melancholy fitted to all this polite mulching. It had never heard of real ragtime. "She dances like an angel," said her husband.

The next morning I left Rome for Naples. I saw the Rome papers later and kept watching the crime news items for a long time but gave up after a while.

Martin was the forgiving type . . .

News bulletins announced from time to time that Addis Ababa was in sight and that Haile Selassie had shaved off his beard and, dressed as Al Jolson (an American Congressman), had fled the country. England had refused to permit the sale of war planes to Abyssinians and had sent the Douche a very stiff set of notes about the use of poison gas on naked natives. Not cricket . . .

V

"My two boys are dead," said the old paper woman.

"I am sorry."

"It is better. Now I no longer worry for the big war."

I folded the newspaper. "You think it is coming?"

"Yes. He says it is coming. Now my boys are dead and I no longer have to worry and sit up nights crying."

"Don't you cry?" I asked like a fool.

"Inside . . . only inside."

"I understand."

"The niggers captured my boys and cut them apart like a hen."

"It is very sad," I said, leaving her.

Chapter 2

EXCERPTS FROM LETTERS OF
THE OIL DRILLER TO CHICO

D<small>EAR</small> C<small>HICO</small>:

Here I am in the new Italian Empire and the natives are hanging like ripe fruit on the gallows under my window. They learn things the hard way from the *Fasci di Combattimento,* only mostly they don't learn at all.

Abyssinia—is it everything they claimed—or isn't it? I haven't found any oil to dig for yet. Maybe I will. Addis Ababa, if you ask me, is not worth all the bother. Ice is sold like diamonds by the pin point—and the odor of black skins is something to remember at bad moments.

The pestilential city of Addis Ababa is always under the enormous blood-orange sun. The Fahrenheit, Centigrade and Réaumur degrees on the thermometer climb like monkeys on a hot pipe. The palpable heat sweeps in from the shadows on the red-orange and pyrite-green hills. The poor, prickly-heated Italian garrisons on the road toward Dijirem, Yirga-Alem and Ginir, suffer.

II

I went for a walk at dawn.

The broad city danced in the red heat haze and the pollarded poplars were ghostly with white dust while the new

gallows are hung with black ripe fruit on hemp stems, twisting with spasmodic turns. Barefooted natives looking up at
the kindness of invaders, stood there saying nothing.

The Mohammedan section has a distinct rhythm of Arab
existence. The broiled skies echo the dung-towers' *La Allah
il Allah* as they bow to Mecca and lament . . .

The pasty, sweat-wet Italian troops marching in sloggy
order pass, the ribbons of bayonets shaking under their
fever; that is the rhythm of life for the poor Italians who
live and fight and die among the acacia and thorn, the
mildew agues and rheumatism of the pelting monsoons.

The *masikas* is over, the Ethiopians come under the daring
Dejazmatch Gabra Howot, from the northwest in Tigré;
and the Dejz Hailu from the provinces of Tembien and
Sokoto, with his devils armed with Lewis guns and dynamite and long knives that had cut six hundred Italian throats
since the scorpions and earwigs had nested. The railway
to Djibouti had been cut for four days. The antelopes and
koodoos and the leering hyenas run over the savannas. Give
me Hell *or* Texas . . .

III

I am still hunting for oil wells to drill. I have some foul
servants, a whole daffy regiment of dying wops and mean
Arabs and enough bad whiskey to turn any liver but a Texas
boy's, to stone. The Romans are dying like flies, the natives
are murdered by the thousands. The women are all pregnant and who knows what they will produce, and the ex-
ploitation of this country is not going so well.

I live in whatever style this place can afford. I get paid.
Most of the wops don't, although the rich boys and the
son-in-laws and relatives of the Douche are stealing everything.

We had fun the last time I went out for oil hunting . . .

I rode on a sad little donkey. There were three hundred mounted Arabs, half a division of dirty blacks, many still moving in a drugged sleep (for they were all hemp smokers and mean and red-eyed). There were two armored cars and a hot, reeking little tank in which the puking pilot would stick his blue face out every half hour and pass out, then wake up and be sick all over again.

We would rest and the blacks would slap at the insect scourges and watch the daws, ibises, quails and moor hens run. The Italian *arditis* looked bad. They were sick men, over-tanned, with deep lacerations of *acacia horrida* and the deep, pitted pock marks of *Rhus toxicodendron,* and at high noon a man died of heat, calling for his mother and he was shoved to a filthy ditch and covered with stones. The going grew hard and we fell into a cleft of impenetrable thickets and interlacing lianas. This was not the wide streets of Rome by a long shot . . .

The rail lines ran, guarded every twenty feet by blacks

and every mile by a hovel of sandbags loaded with machine guns, more blacks, unshaved Italians in a stupor from heat and wine and fear of death and disease.

We threw away the tank (for the driver could not be revived) and we went on toward a graveyard among dusty cypresses, a cemetery and one of the best-kept I had ever seen. A lot of Italians are here for keeps. *Mangi et taci.*

Another sandbag hovel was here, a large one with many railroad rails and six Italians in better rags than the private soldiers. Over a camel-dung fire there was food and we ate and the men had some bad wine, but biting, and they talked about the powers that were, while a hot wind ran over the long sere grass and sweat ran off them in amber globules and their breaths stank . . .

We were served by dark-skinned Kisemo girls, shiny, satiny, in the natural semi-nude of the land. Their over-extended charms and steatopygian rumps seemed to be old stories to the officers who were even tired of making love (which they prefer to war) . . .

Later we crossed a blue clay ridge and, across the heat valley, saw the silver ribbons of the rails end in a clot of dead bodies, and camel riders and armored cars stood around, and far off in the mauve-gray hills we saw specks moving against the luminous blue sky. No one followed the raiders for it was hot and dry and everyone was very frightened . . .

A hundred feet of rail had been ripped up, heated and twisted around telegraph poles and a hundred Italians would never go back to their grape arbors . . .

The rail lines are always in danger but our only safety lay in sticking near them in case the natives rushed us in great numbers. It all sounds very romantic and daring, I suppose, but it *ain't*—pal.

IV

We were out four weeks this time . . .

Night came, and flares went up around the sandbagged
hovels but the heat stayed and the stars came, too—a con-
stellation of little pin pricks and a half-strangled mad moon.
Lights marked the fires of the rail guards—a thousand miles
of rail thus protected. And the night still to grow darker.

As the darkness of the cypress and the huge drum of the
night grew darker, my men eyed the hills and watched with
care, with tremendous care, the hills. From there would
come death and a lot of fancy by-play and sport . . .

V

Texas, here I come—home . . . ! I'm heading home and
to hell with wop gold. The train was the only one through
in two weeks and I took it. It was marked with huge Red
Crosses and they could fill a hundred like it. It's a favor
here to lend a man a razor to cut his throat with.

A long line of men appeared with stretchers full of groaning wretches. Malignant fever, pullulating madness; groaning, cursing wounded were banged aboard and the mad, unwashed wretches in the terrible heat stank across half a mile
of thorny growths and unfurrowed fields (and we held
our noses and pitied them).

I was given a small, square room with a small window
almost covered with armored plate and we started with a
jerk and the low light of the camps fell away and we ran
at slow speed along the foothills of steep declivities and I
was a very hot, happy guy . . .

A silvery, dirty color covered everything and I could
neither smoke nor read. No lights was the rule and it began
suddenly to rain and the rain lisped on against the roof

and the train went forward like a tired horse in a low, crouching stride and the land looked cruel and evil . . .

We stopped now and then to drop off the dead men at sandbagged hovels (for meat spoils quickly here). A little Greek came through the train and called me *Savvid offendi* and offered coffee. We drank.

There was an attack just before dawn. I suppose a serious one. I couldn't see much. I was sleeping wetly in my own juices and someone howled and someone cursed and I heard things and *there,* far away, were horsemen . . .

There were hundreds of them, dark faced, lean, well armed and evil looking. The Ethiopians were raiding the rail lines again, I supposed, but they were behind us and the train would get through—but the camps, the sandbag hovels, the black troops from the coast, the sick wops and the general would get hell for a long time.

Then, at dawn, I saw a burnt offering for a landscape;

guerrillas spotting the hills. There were quick marching, sick, Italian farm boys, some dying and being shoved into a ditch, and a man tied to a stretcher.

The rain was almost steam, we ran across the border, across to the French hold on the broad, black, sprawling belly of Africa. The azure sky and the khaki hills were still one with heat and there was no let-up and as the enormous blood ball of the sun came up, it hit me hard. . . .

VI

At Port Said there was a wire that two thousand Italians had found their destiny in Africa in a month—their destiny and their graves. Only the officers, however, are planted in nice, shimmering graveyards. *Pax Romana!* Oh, those *diavoli neri*—the black devils—are real killers.

I think I'll head for home via India. There is talk of new drillings in Burma, and Standard Oil civilization has made easy pickings for men of my ilk. Give my love to Emma if you should ever see her. My guess: the next blow-off is Spain or France . . .

NATIVE SON

It was a small boat running between the islands, and someone had told me some lies about some rare ruins and I had been there. There were no ruins (except of an old cinema palace). The small fat Italian ran around with a box of dreadful ice cream, and he also sold copies of *The Saturday Evening Post* and shined shoes and helped the boat crew lift the iron gates when cars drove on board.

"How is business?" I asked, knowing it would please him.

"Vera good."

"Better than in Italy . . . they say."

"Listen . . . Italy one damn bigga nation."

"Sure . . . if that's what you want to be."

"I prouda."

"You have any sons fighting in Africa?"

"My sista she hava three sons and two sons-in-law there."

"Ask your sister what she thinks about the new Italy."

"She like."

"When you going back there?"

"Listen you think me damn fool."

"Oh."

"Me American, you betcha . . . vota solid ticket every time."

"What ticket?"

"Only *one* solid ticket . . . one who pay two bucks."

The boat bumped into the rotting wooden pier. England was firing sanctions against Italy. The British Home Fleet was in port . . .

Chapter 3

THOMAS COOK'S

Tʜᴇ *lush little clerk rattled his colored travel folders,
pointed to the nerve ends and muscles of the world and
looked at Chico's necktie—his second best tie—and said:*
   "*Everyone is going to Cannes this year to avoid* la lotia di
class—*the class struggle.*"
   "*It's a little too rich for me,*" *said Chico shyly.*
   "*There is always Nice, nice and* chic."
   "*I want an island.*"
   "*Capri is well spoken of.*"
   "*Too well.*"
   "*The Iles d'Hyères, Sardinia, ah*—here *is Majorca.*"
   "*Majorca, that sounds like it.*"
   *So Chico went to Majorca . . . and wrote in his journal
of* "the lazy sleeping dago lands . . ."

MAJORCA

That year there was a girl at Palma, on Majorca, who had
very wide eyes and I used to take her to old Iviza's *fonda*
. . . the best damn inn on the island, and feed her *cala de
sobreasada* and watch the sweat form on her lovely upper
lip as she ate and we used to walk by the blue sea, that wide

44

Mediterranean, where I would kiss her and take those permitted Mediterranean liberties. And late at night listening to the *zombomba* players flouting Plato, and calling Pan from the hills, I would tell her about the world, and take her home and kiss her, and kiss her aunt good-night, and go back to the little white house rented from the *alpargata* maker, who made the best rope-soled sandals in all the Balearic Islands . . . and think about the book I was writing and how badly it was going . . . while the nations of the world, like great cats, sat watching each other . . .

But I was younger then—not much younger, true . . . but young enough to keep writing and one day the newspapers came. There was a revolt against the Republic on the mainland—something the damn fool radio had been bumbling about, too—but no one had paid it much attention. Radio, to hell with it—said the *alpargata* maker—a miserable genie popping out of ginger ale bottles. But now the shopkeeper put on his uniform and the cork king and the olive oil tsar, all got out their guns and said they were the seed of rich rebellious men and were taking over for General Franco, and somebody had to shoot them in the stomach and they died hard and in pain. I saw it wasn't going to be like it had been. Not any more for a while, anyway. A cable came for me and I was suddenly a man of importance—representative for an American press service, ordered to Barcelona to write of the Civil War. And I didn't like that. The revolt of the bankers and landowners and Church had become official and was in capital letters. But it was no time to reconnoitre one's leisure.

And on the boat, when Cape Formentor dropped behind, I thought of the girl with sweat on her upper lip eating *cala de sobreasada* ... and I remembered the contents of the dish—the sweet dough, the sweet diced peppers and the paprika pork sausage.

The girl hadn't been so important after all ...

BARCELONA

As the harbor came into view, the chipped white Greek ship slowed her speed and I saw the city as I remembered it. I felt happy to be back. Even if there had been bloody battles in the streets, and a great many workers and dock heavers and butcher boys and officers in corsets and mill owners and hotel head waiters had died. There was a sinuous rhythmic twitching of sound and now the Republic had the city and I wanted to know and wanted to see all. I was very much like a school boy trying to impress the high school football coach the first time out for practise. A warm wind blew an acetylene-garlic odor mixed with mimosa and alluvial soil ...

II

A tall thin man in hairy tweeds, with red-rimmed eyes, and yellow, tobacco-stained fingers that shook like those of a harp player at work, stood by the very pretty girl with a matched set of healthy shapely legs, and he didn't bother to stop reading from the little volume of Anton Chekhov's letters:

"The middle class is very fond of so called practical types and novels with happy endings, since they are soothed with the idea that one can both accumulate capital and preserve innocence, be a beast and at the same time happy . . ."

The girl turned and pulled some strands of her very red hair that the wind had thrown into her teeth and said to me in the subtle fugitive qualities her voice had:

"Make him stop reading, Chico."

"Show him the way to the bar, Annabelle," I answered, gathering my blankets and portable typewriter and drawing-kit, as the hoarse thunder of the boat whistle blew for the pier. A pungent flavor of bay leaves came from the hold—a rose-madder sail passed us.

The tall thin man, his red nose like a ragged carrot, smiled and closed his book. The sweet ponderous flapping of bells came from Barcelona.

"I can see this is the first bit of war flim-flam you two have been on . . ."

"Good old Shad Roe," said the girl Annabelle. "He's bored to death with wars—in the pig's pink eye!"

Shad Roe looked at his shaking hands. "I am. I've been out since the Boer War reporting the clash of battle. I've seen dead men and broken houses, and horses with their backs smashed; I've seen dead Dutchmen and dead tommies and dead matlos, and in the Boxer mix-up, every kind of dead man—white, yellow and brown. I've been famous for what I wrote about Mons, and I invented the angels-in-the-sky story, and Verdun is almost as much my battle as that old dung-beetle's—Pétain's."

"This is different," I said.

"Yes," said Annabelle, sending off a jaunting perfume. "This is to save the Republic."

"Join me in a snifter. We'll drink to luck and gory details. Always give the newspaper readers—dull dogs—give them gory details and plenty of zip. Editors love it—it helps them fight constipation."

We went into the dirty bar, roaches bigger than cigars waved at us, the dirty little yellow man from Java, who was barman, mixed us the last of the Scotch in the last of the muddy drinking water and we drank and my spinal marrow ached with the idea of action.

III

A small boat flying a red flag, with Spanish lettering on it, came alongside, floating on weedy sea wrack and spermy sea drift and three men in blue overalls and carrying rifles came up the side, and one—a big boy with dark hair—had his brow tied up in a bloody bandage. They came into the bar and asked for our papers, and they looked at them and asked us if we had any fascists and we said no and we bought them a drink of white wine. Shad Roe gave them cigars and the ship moved slowly on that fruit-green water and the heat made hotter the chipped white sides of the Greek boat. The blue overalls watched us with a cat-like potency.

"It's all right now?" asked Shad Roe.

"It is," said the Bloody Bandage. "Like a *fiesta*. They are showing Franco in the newsreels."

"Was it very hard?"

"For three days—*malo*. I tell you it was like nothing at all—just shooting in the streets, catch the bastards—*hijos de putas*—and standing them up and shooting them, and they catching us and shooting us."

"And now?"

"It's fine. We have the city and are organizing Workers' Guards and they are leaving town dressed as workers and herders and priests. *Huervas!* We can't catch all of them— only those that load up with gold and paintings. They love paintings."

"Yes, don't they?" said Shad Roe.

"And money—how they love money. They can't win. We fight for Republic of Spain, you know." He looked a little worried as if he wanted to be correct and meticulous with strangers—but had ethics and senses of his own.

"I know," I said.

"Sure, you must come ashore. You have brought no fascists. I know. It will soon be over. Everyone who works is arming. Even the little boys, smoking their *pitillos*—they carry a gun and stand guard. It is very pleasant to see people defending their Republic."

We had more white wine and then the men went away after shaking hands, *Macho*. Annabelle rubbed a run in her stocking.

"That one with the bashed-in skull is very cute. I think I'll wait for him at the pier. Get details of the fighting from him."

"Keep away from spicks," said Shad Roe, drinking down his wine, his cheeks turning blue. "You can't ever know what they'll do if they think you a déclassé bitch. They make love like whips landing. Why not be kind to a fellow Englishman?"

"I don't like your shirt collars," she said and we sent
the yellow boy looking for a bottle of blue wine. The ship
was tossing mooring ropes onto the pier. They had two
machine guns mounted and an old French seventy-five, and
the men in blue overalls sat around over a *bota* skin full of
purple stuff, drinking and rolling brown paper cigarettes,
and the city looked very calm, only a fat man in black lay
very dead on his back under a lamp post and a dog stopped
to talk to him, and a stucco tower over a cork warehouse
sat sideways like a hat on a drunkard, I thought. Shad Roe
drank and Annabelle fixed herself a new mouth out of red
lard and as yet we saw no tangible living enemy of the
Republic . . .

IV

We couldn't go ashore yet. They were hunting the ship
carefully because the fascists were slipping priests into
Spain loaded with gold money belts to finance Franco and
his Moors, and I didn't blame them for being careful.

Flat-hung symbols of hills stood far off.

Shad Roe fascinated me. I had been used to the Front-
Page type of reporter, all wise-crack and bluster, the shallow
ooze of small minds stirring into existence—but Shad Roe
(he was very fond of fish life and ate with great grinding
joy the roe and milts of many fish, and after that drank as
much as he could get to fight a giant thirst and so prepared
himself for more fish roe)—Shad Roe was an Englishman,
a classical scholar, and they still speak of him with great
pride at Oxford, and he could write Latin verse (a fearful
curse, I thought) and he was a fine reporter, only he said:
"Journalist, chappie." I liked him—a delicious, indispensable
lush—and feared him and wondered how he managed to
stay alive after forty years of internal alcohol baths. He never

sweated, lost his temper, got fighting drunk nor raised his voice. He believed in nothing, hated nothing, loved everybody and wrote the kind of prose they liked in Fleet Street. Very dull reading. And he sang one song: *Giovinezza, giovinezza, primavera di bellezza.*

V

Annabelle had joined us at Carlos de la Rapita at the mouth of the silt-choked Ebro River. She was from Teignmouth in Devon and had a face like fine Sèvres china . . . not at all as English as I had expected, and she painted fearful water-colors for *Vogue,* and wrote little stories about Spanish cooking and the art of basket-weaving on Corsica, and who had been sleeping together at Monte and what the Duchess said to the Countess at Antibes ("What's your gimmick, toots?"). And little magazines and gossip columns reprinted her, and she read Russian novels and wrote poems in the manner—but not the content—of T. S. Eliot (whom she knew very well and called a crashing, bigoted genius). She couldn't sing, but howled *O Tannenbaum, O Tannenbaum, wir treu sind deine Blätter* after her second brandy.

With these two singers, my only vocal refrain—*Darling Nellie Gray*—was voted a "bloody brick."

I liked Annabelle and wondered if she was very mad or deep—and doubted that she could ever write an intelligent report about anything she saw of the revolt. (And in time she wrote the best stuff sent out of Spain that year, and some people say she influenced the minds and styles of Dotty Thompson and a woman called Clare Boothe, when those ladies followed her small, narrow, toe-less shoes into reporting the state of the world. But Annabelle never made any money from her writing and never wanted to, and I

liked the way she refused to write a book or to be photo-
graphed in tailored, pressed Fifth Avenue slacks aiming an
unloaded camera at Chiang Kai-shek. She liked traveling,
and dimpled beautifully across the buttocks.)

VI

Suddenly as the ship rested like a tired elephant against
the pier, there was the sound of shellfire in the city and
then a big black mushroom of smoke came from the center
of Barcelona, and bits of stone and stucco began to fly from
the flanks of buildings near us and sirens sounded and lots
of trucks started running down the streets. Men in overalls
with red arm bands and shotguns and service rifles ran after
them. Then suddenly it was very still again and a little dirty
barefooted girl came out to us with a basket of golden
oranges and asked us to buy some. The city fell fitfully like
a bad sleeper back to stillness. The men at the seventy-five
made more brown paper cigarettes and the fat dead man in

black rested very still on his back, his toes carefully turned in, and Shad Roe picked up a fresh book, looked at Annabelle fixing her hair, and began to read . . .

> Le squelette était invisible
> Au temps heureux de l'art païen!

And that's how silly and simple it was in those days to go to a war.

They let us ashore. Annabelle took the arm of Bloody Bandage and asked him if his head hurt and Shad Roe and I went to a hotel and had a bath and went out into the street to meet the people of the Republic; where Daumier drawings sold newspapers by much shouting.

Annabelle joined us at dinner, and we went to see a children's home where the fascists had raped and shot three nurses. And late at night I heard planes in the sky, and some place, far off, someone threw a bomb and I wondered at this strangeness and variety and if all this meant anything important enough to give up my only life for . . .

WHO IS FOR WHAT?

It is easy to find out anything you want to know. Just ask. We are at what passes for the Ritz Hotel here, and very swanky it is, but a little smelly, and the help has all gone into the streets to find guns. You see them along the Paseo, the Ramblas, the Plaza da Catuluna . . . men in dress shirts still looking like waiters, and busboys in white—all mixed up with men in blue overalls with arm bands.

A little professor of Iberian history was carrying a Lewis gun and it was very heavy, so I gave him a lift and he thanked me and we sat on the curb watching truck loads of men passing, shouting "Frente Popular!" as loud and as often as they could.

"They look happy," I said.

The little professor smiled. "Why not? They love the Republic."

"And the other side?"

"Let us be fair," said the little professor. "They love their Spain, too . . . their rich land, fields, bonds, apartment houses, big cars, paintings, easy comfort . . . It's just too bad there is not room for both without taking it out on the people of Spain. A few of them, against millions of us."

"I don't understand it. I'm new to all this revolt."

"It's simple. On Saturday, July eighteenth, nineteen-thirty-six, the Second World War started when Franco and his generals brought over their Moors and Foreign Legion degenerates. Remember he is fighting almost entirely with Moors and outlanders—until his kind rally to him."

"Who is joining him?"

"The rich Catholics, monarchists, fascists, insurgent generals . . ."

"And with you?"

"The poor Catholics, almost to a man. The women sometimes follow the skirts of their priests. The republicans are with us, the liberals, all the liberal democratic regime and socialists, syndicalists, workers' unions, Nationalist Catalans, Basque autonomists, people's militia . . . in fact, everyone who loves the trees and skies of Spain and not the damn Jesuits whose holdings in Spain had torn five hundred million dollars from the people."

"That's how it divides up?" I asked.

"About that way."

"The arm bands they wear here—and the blue overalls . . . ?"

"Well, the men in blue overalls—they are the little people. Shopkeepers, farmers, workers, printers, waiters, teachers—in fact, anybody who loves the Republic. As for arm

bands—those marked *Trabajadores* are socialist—very democratic in ideals, most of them. *Confederacion Nacional de
Trabajo* are the syndicalists—dreamers, mostly—but hard,
violent dreamers who know how to fight. *Federacion Anar-
quista Iberia* are the anarchists. They don't vote or take part
in national politics. They don't believe in that. They just
want to be let alone. But they've joined up to fight for the
Republic."

"Where are the reds?"

He looked at me and smiled. "You've been listening to
the French and English radios again. Spain never was very
red. There are a few Moscow followers—but mostly the
radicals are Spanish in name and culture. Franco is howling
about reds—what they do to churches, nuns, tennis players,
blue ribbon dogs. There hasn't been much terror yet . . . Oh,
we'll get hard if they do. But keep your eyes open—stay
honest."

"What makes you think this is the beginning of World War II?"

"Stay around and find out. England, France and America can prevent it leading to that. I am an old man. I carry a machine gun. But this war will be decided in Downing Street, in the White House, in the Wilhelmstrasse. If Franco wins, you Americans will die by the hundreds of thousands to stay free."

He was a very old man and a little touched, I felt. I went away quickly . . .

THE FRIEND

"Oh dear," said the little lady. "Are they shooting again?"

"Yes," I said. "Why don't you go back to America?"

"I can't. I'm poor."

"How long have you been here?"

"Twenty-two years."

"What do you do for money?"

"I'm a friend. I answer ads in the papers."

"For friends?"

"Rich English women or Americans . . . when they need someone to travel with . . . I go."

"I don't think you'll get any trade this year."

"Then I shall starve. But they'll come."

"The rich?"

"Yes."

I gave her my arm and we went in to dinner.

Chapter 4

THE FRONT

Aɴᴅ *every place during that era of progressive degradation that Chico went, and Shad Roe went along, the front
changed. Near Cervera they were very nice to him but said
they couldn't let any reporters out to the front. Chico said
he wasn't a reporter, anyway, but a writer, a fragmentary
Proust knocking at the doors of the Book-of-the-Month
Club.*

   "Could you speak a lot of things, like French and English?"
   "English I'm a devil at," said Chico.
   "And German?"
   "I can puff with the best. Sometimes I understand it."
   "We could use an interpreter."
   And that is how Chico really joined the Loyalist armies ...

WAR IN SPAIN

At first a man doesn't know and doesn't care too much
about sides. And I went along and acted like an expert in
many things and spoke some sort of German and a lot of
English and translated German hotel ads for the general
staff. And always the army in blue overalls marched. The
few planes they had went up and died in the sky—and so
we went along and hoped the war would end and the Republic would be saved and infuriated gestures stopped.

England and France were very fair—no coarse persuasive-
ness—and choked off almost everything they could that
would help the fellow Democratic Republic, and winked and
turned the other way when the Nazis and Wops came over
to help the Moors murder Christian peasants defending their
elected government. "Country Club Christianity in France
and England"—said Shad Roe once—"can never win a war
again."

II

So the winter passed and I wrote to Annabelle and Shad
Roe in Madrid, and then one day I saw a lot of little girls
with their throats cut and their dresses neatly replaced over
little stomachs opened up by Moorish bayonets, and after
that I marched with the troops and got shot at and ran very
unheroically, and then I learned a lot of things about killing and by spring I was ready for the big advance they were
planning.

It was silly of me to become involved. I didn't even know
the names of the murdered little girls . . .

III

That spring the heavy silver mountains that hemmed us
in had festered with men and guns and the hoof-hiss of
flop-eared burros, cheerful under curses and big burdens.
Now heavy artillery and tanks—grumbling with flat-footed
speed, were tearing deep ruts in the mountain trails as they
passed, reeking of white gas smoke. Many regiments of
strange brown men were coming along under the dusty
broken olive trees—their equipment rattling and the polished
rifle butts and ugly-nosed machine guns growing like deadly
fungus out of their backs; the bright glowing ends of their
cigarettes, limp on dusty lips . . .

Overhead droned the heavy purr of pursuit planes—ours for a change—and far ahead in the deep purple hills, bearded in heavy firs, there was the troubled rumble of rapid fire and sudden flames in dark shadows. All spring, men had faced each other across the red unplowed earth and sent death in whining volleys over each other's dead.

We had lived—or rather existed—in our fox holes among the simple humble debris of war-making—but the enemy and our generals were feeling the whisper of the spring— the rank green grass and the heavy night odors of wet ground and growing plants. So they stirred over lampshaded maps and ordered progress. . . .

We held—or tried to hold—a hundred miles of zigzag front that protected the valley—so fruitful behind us. The white shell of the town house—gutted by the Moors' fires— was like a kind white father behind us—and on our left and right, the mountains leered down upon us, heavy with unburied dead and seared by shell fire into bald gray spots.

We knew that life was a slender thread when the walking wounded of our outposts began to dribble back in doped logginess, and the bright message of wounds—red on arms and legs, filled to overflowing the shaking Red Cross flivvers. Then came the stretcher-bearers, sweating in grunting fear, their gory loads stone-still or screaming—fragments of men that had marched from Madrid so short a time ago, to the cheers and lusty hugs of the women, and the dry throaty sobs and streaming cheeks of the old folks . . .

IV

The lisp of the phone holes us out of the smashed village square and orders us to the front in a silver cold dawn, as the lazy sun sends rays into the massed clouds. We load fifty extra rounds each, down the soggy doughy mess of breakfast, and with the last pint of sour wine gurgling in our bellies, move up to the growing confusion of the lines. Three lines go forward, with the slog of many feet. We make a fourth.

Yellow Trenchcoat—a dirty, once white muffler under his copper wire of a beard—lights the last gasper in his pack and growls a yellow-toothed smile as he shades his eyes and looks over the twisting road ahead.

"They want this valley, but so do we."

Cherrynose wipes his namesake on a sleeve and belches up the winey gas. "This valley, or any valley—they can have them all. What good is land if you don't plant on it?"

I grin and spit out the hot dry dust of the road from my mouth. "Cherrynose misses the blooded oxen of his cabbage farm and the warm mellow pleasures of wedded life."

"Ah—what know you, city lice, of the soil of Spain—the furrows under the steel plow, the rank wood smoke under a fresh-killed hog, and the shirtless babies on the dirt floor plucking feathers out of the squawking rooster, while a big-breasted, bare-footed wife stirs the onion soup?"

Yellow Trenchcoat growls. "We know enough about Spanish soil to fight for it. Close up and I'll tear the man apart that throws away any rifle shells in the ditch."

A staff car, all mud and painted slogans, pulls to a stop with a scream of tormented brakes and a long thin man, bent over the cobweb drawings of an H.Q. map, rasps at us from under a pampered mustache.

"Where is the Hill of Sweet Flowers?"

Big Stomach scratches himself under the armpits and points to the shattered pock-marked hillside on which the barbwire is threaded with bright blops of shredded rags.

"That's the hill, and those things on the wire are all the flowers that are left."

"Don't pick them—they're mined."

Long Thin Man adds a pair of glasses to his nose, and over them looks at us.

"Remember, men, that the Republic needs every shoulder to the wheel. You are facing Moors that have raped their way here up from the coast. We must clear the valley— you are the strength of Spain and in you she glories."

Yellow Trenchcoat makes a sound by puckering his lips and, far down the line, the Crazy Kid lifts his mouth to the sky, and with mad fingers starts his banjo strings vibrating as he jars the air with *The General Dies in Bed*. The whole staggering column—four hundred strong—takes up the re-frain that concludes with the news that the general died in bed—but not alone.

The staff car starts with a neck-breaking jar and the last we see of the tall thin officer is his turkey-red face twisted into angry speech, holding on for dear life.

Cherrynose sighs.

"Always speeches at the front; and in the cities the gay young lads sit at corner cafés drinking up our wines, praising the brave proletariat and thinking up slogans."

It is a short crude word that Yellow Trenchcoat uses to tell us what he thinks the lads in cities are. We plod along—the hot brave disk of the sun cooking our very marrow. The oily sweat of the pack-bands cut into me and the last of my

muddy water bottle is empty. Tanks growl past. Heavy foreign monsters, reeking of oil and hot steel—the sea-sick pilots retching, their capped heads out of small hatch-holes and holding on with blue-nailed fingers, look most unhappy.

"Stick your damn head in, you turtles."

"May I use your rest room?"

"You'll get yours, you stinking infantry."

"Like men then—not like worms in steel drawers."

"Shut up and keep that line."

V

The tanks pass like circus elephants—theirs flanks rocking in the rutted road. We follow and others follow us. All the valley is moving forward. Anti-aircraft—field hospitals —wire stringers and the noisy arrogant dispatch bearers on ill-balanced motor bikes that shatter eardrums with their roar. The road is tree high in yellow dust and the sharp

stomach-gripping shatter of shellfire comes louder as the wind shifts and brings us the hot odor of battle and the acid bite of millions in fired munitions, but we always find fortunes in more munitions waiting to receive us . . .

We pass the first dead of the battle lying in knotted agony among bloody battered weeds. One man rests in death on his knees and shoulders—perhaps looking for his missing head. All others lie on their backs watching the changing lake-blue sky—as if worried about the weather. They need not worry

—it's a glad gay day, like new red wine—but none of us watches the sky. None of us hears the birds or avoids the roadside orange flowers with clumping feet . . .

VI

Our mouths open and breathe in and we lean forward to lick beef-red lips. Suddenly we feel a great wind and overhead an express train crashes past its station. A blinking maroon ball grows larger with a roar and I smell the burning wood of tormented trees; there is a great whistle that jars the eardrums and just ahead of me poor Drippy turns around with an amazed brown mask on his face and a sharp star-shaped shell fragment in his right eye. He speaks of his God with a gush of bright blood, then folds up like a jack-knife and his tattered heels do a fast drum beat in the chrome-yellow dust. Soon he dies, and the blue star-shaped shell fragment in his right eye is still. I step over him—and Cherrynose flips his finger from nose to navel and from nipple to nipple on his barrel chest, in the sign of a fast cross —and follows in my footsteps. My eyes are dry. We just shiver and hitch at our guns.

The Captain chews on his cigar and the hard corners of his mouth grow even harder. He and Drippy ran a taxi stand; partners in Valencia. Also, his only sister is now a widow with two little girls . . .

We bunch up with fear as we think of Drippy's end—but a short curse from Yellow Trenchcoat, who was twenty years a sergeant in the French Foreign Legion, scatters us into hard-to-hit spacing. The swearing does us good—we swear back from our dry mouths and go on slowly, wondering who will be next. We all think no shell or bullet has our number on it. How could we go on otherwise?

VII

At the edge of the green woods—right beside the two dead white horses—we receive three hand grenades each and clip them on over our growling stomachs. Ahead there is a hell—as if all Spain were on fire. The Captain lights a new cigar and Yellow Trenchcoat and he bend heads over their watches and nod with polite bobs across the swelling horses. Big Stomach rubs the only steel helmet in the group. He swiped it from a poor dying Italian boy, whom the hill dogs had been nibbling on for days. He smiled when Big Stomach, with delicate mercy, tearfully pumped two Luger slugs into his smashed face and then took his steel helmet. Big Stomach chews the corner off a moldy square of gray chocolate and offers me some.

I shake my head and duck as the whine of a German air engine sounds beyond the battle-stained cypress trees. From long experience we bounce down in the roadside grass, and watch the calm fast movements of the Captain as he and Yellow Trenchcoat point the snobbish thin nose of the American machine gun skyward. We don't have long to wait.

There is the crunch and zizz of an incendiary bomb as the yellow trees bow in crimson flames, and straight across the hot-faced sun flash the polished wings of the German airship —big, black and fast—two ground-strafing guns pour fast-spinning belts of bullets down on us in a steel rain. Our machine guns answer without much hope of a hit . . . and the plane comes lower and I feel the thud of foreign slugs dig deep little graves in the soil of Spain. Down our whole earth-hugging rows glides the airman and, like a watering can, he sprays us in garden formation. We do not answer. Only new troops take the trouble to return the fire with their rifles . . .

VIII

The planes pass. A red-haired boy—some whisper he came from America (from a place called Rutgers) to fight —is choking in a deep rut. Pink foam comes from his mouth and his chest is moth-eaten with holes. He gurgles like a water pipe of Turkish design. We can do nothing for him. His own blood in his lungs is drowning him.

A little brown man cheerfully holds up a red ribboned paw and trots quickly to the rear . . . We watch him with a tight pain in our throats and decide that in twenty lucky minutes he will be back in the village . . . We all pray for a light wound and finger our cartridge belts . . .

We hurry on—and a strange song sings in my ears. A tank gutted by fire blocks our path—we walk around it. The seared, plucked torso—nothing else—of its lone crew lies beside it. The dead are thicker now and all lie on their backs and watch the sky. Some, lightly wounded, whimper among the bushes, and far up the road a horse screams in pawing pain and comes toward us. We split apart and it grinds past us dragging sagging, pink and white, blue-veined secrets with it.

A man retches into the ditch and suddenly the Captain yells through the big mouth he has enlarged by funneling his two hands to his face.

"Fix bayonets. Double time. We take the hill ahead and hold it until the seventy-fives come up. No stragglers."

Yellow Trenchcoat reloads his Mauser and growls to us:

"Keep your noggins down and your bayonets in front. If you're hit, stay down—I don't want any heroes."

The cruel coolness of bare steel goes on my rifle with surprisingly steady hands. I feel silly as the beads of sweat run down my sun-stained nose and I wish with all my soul for water . . .

A whistle sounds—silly piping against the full volume of shelling. The hills loom ahead but I see nothing except a bulk of heat-hazed shrubbery, and high up the angry spit of machine guns nested with great cunning to flay all who approach. We walk faster now, remembering deaths and past battles. Soon we are running, and from our rasped throats there is a nameless shouting grunt—half laugh, half snarl, that none of us seems to be able to repeat later on when, in calmer moments, we talk about it. My feet push the ground behind me and I keep going, leaning way over, sweating until it burns down my torso from under my armpits. My mouth is wide open and I scream—but I hear nothing. Up ahead, the office chatter of friendly typewriters sounds, and I know I'm walking into machine guns. I am in a blue funk. I am young—I am in love with life—but I keep going. I keep yelling; I keep running . . . all others do the same. The crackle of my companions surrounds me. All face death; all keep going forward. Why? Trained old line soldiers go forward on orders—without reason . . .

IX

Two men go down on my right. One throws arms high in a cheer leader style and glides down like a ballet master finishing a difficult step, the other is suddenly stopped with a thud, as the slug grunts into him, and turns quickly, surprise in his wide blue eyes, and he hits the ground a hard blow, turns over on his back, and eyes the sky slack-mouthed. All seem to die on their backs. I look around. Yes, all the dead are on their backs. I make up a game—I hunt for a dead man lying on his face. I see none. Suddenly I find I am hovering over a machine gun nest, tucked into a brown leaf-strewn hole. Three men lie in a small stale hole, digging and caressing the steel secrets of a water-cooled machine gun.

Under coal-pail helmets, their dirty red fingers coax the belts of bullets into the clattering tool and keep up a steady burst against my friends. Suddenly, I flex all over in a deadly game. I am calm now.

I tug with numb fingers and pick a grenade from my belt. The metal ring tastes salty in my mouth as I pull the firing pin and release it. I slowly count to four—then, with a wide

walloping heave, I throw and grind my whole being into the soft ground until my face is mashed deep in the dusty mold. I smell decay and the sweet stench of shallow graves.

Far away, and like a fairy tale of long ago—there is crimson rumple and I think of Jack and the Beanstalk. Clouds of black earth shower down on me and I wish they would bury me and I could sleep like the Babes in the Woods. All is over now except the heavy sharpness of smoke.

A scream floats over and I am on my knees peeping

ahead. The nest of the three gunners is gone. The sun is gone. Only a few pink shreds of flesh are seen and the pale dirty face, deeply freckled, of a long-armed torso. Legs, there are none—only bloody rags. The Thing lifts itself up on its arms and the deep red mouth screams at me. I come in fast, my bayonet first, and aim for the throbbing throat. I gag—but push the steel home and down with a professional twist of the wrist. The steel flicks out bright rusted and I stumble on, wondering why life seems so simple. Kill or be killed.

I throw the rest of my bombs. I yell and far ahead see the yellow trenchcoat of my sergeant darting in wild glee among gun barrels. Demons yell around me and I yell back and pour flames down on flushed faces in a shallow trench. They swallow fire and sag down to the floor. Tanks, small ones— like mailed nervous whippets, come toward us. We go down gasping, and wait, as they clank like cheap iron pots. Big Stomach reaches for pint bottles of gasoline and winks. He yells at me and laughs. I hear nothing but grin back and nod. Big Stomach is a card—and an anti-tank expert, self-taught.

Big Stomach stands up and thumbs short stubby fingers to a broad pock-marked nose and wriggles his pinkie with glee. A tank glides toward him. He roars with joy; he is very happy and his mirth is almost beyond control. With perfect calm, he throws three fast bottles under the tank. The glass flashes in shattered fragments against the sun's rays and then Big Stomach throws a nicely controlled bomb and we all stop and wait.

The tank disappears in a blinding roar of flame. It rears back like a bronco and plops down and opens like an oyster as the flight of fast flames shrouds it in fire . . . Two men, banging fire out of their hair, are propelled from the tank and Big Stomach grins and calmly shoots them down with two expert tosses of his Luger. We hate tanks. We see something unfair in their use—we make no move to stop Big Stomach.

Two more tanks are blasted out in flames and the others turn tail and rattle off with much noise—but little urge to fight the gasoline pints.

X

We go on with thinner ranks; many old comrades are down. I swear and swing my gun butt at a hand aiming a pistol at me. The bones crack and the fingers fan out. Someone behind me sends down a bayonet and finishes my work for me with a slither and grunt . . .

I can get no air. My mouth is wide open. I gag and gasp —only fire glides down my throat and I dream I am drowning—but I stop in mid-pleasure and fling myself forward as the sinister warning of concussion announces a shell. I am slapped hard down until I mouth the hot leaf-molded dust. I am shaken like a rat in a terrier's teeth, I bounce against the ground, turn over on my back and stay there looking at the hot dome of the blue sky. Cotton clouds mass and move —but no birds sing. I am dead like all dead today—dead on my back, waiting for the burial squad—if the hill dogs don't scent me first . . .

I will not die and I fool them by turning on my stomach. My heart is still pumping and I am amazed that a dead man should have such a wonderfully active organ. I am a marvelous dead man indeed. Blood sings in my ears; my lungs flap air like a fresh caught trout; I can even feel the bite of sour wine from my last meal. Every little nerve stands on end and begs for attention. I am dewed in sweat. For a dead man, I am very much alive. Too much. The world is a red daze of fire and nothing seems to be in focus. Little brown leaves float lazily down on me as the shears of yellow gun fire clip them in ragged patterns and peel the twigs until the pale green of the underbark shows.

I feel my arms glow as they rub my face, and with dainty care I explore my torso and the soft dimples of my numb stomach. The lean legs are solid and no red seepage announces any wound. The shell was close, but not close enough. I get up and stagger on toward the fight. Why, I don't know or care much. Soldiers are silly sheep and once the first few battles are over, will keep going, come what may, as long as they can draw breath and move limbs to fire and walk . . .

XI

A bitter acrid wind strikes me and the sun draws blinking tears from my eyes that taste salty in the tight corners of my mouth. The top of the hill at last. Cadavers lie about—and I find them here at last on their stomachs. One doesn't count —a tank has flattened him out and I inspect the results with interest—then gag. A few shapes stir and the sting of gun flashes twitches them into stillness. Three men pass—green-faced—their pink dirty hands high, mouthing silly words of mercy from between blue lips. They pass and I throw myself down between Cherrynose and Big Stomach. The stench of trench odors comes to me and I hug a soggy sand bag and look over the horizon of sky and deep dropping plain. Heat shimmer shows a few old rag-bags, running fast. One trips and falls in a pinwheel of arms and legs as the sudden concussion of bullets flings him earthward. Far off some tanks rumble their heavy steel buttocks to the rear and we lie, breathing and waiting for the counter-attack. A barrage is firing behind us—but, as usual, it is short and falls too near us. We curse and duck.

Yellow Trenchcoat comes around the corner of the trench,

a flap of face-skin bloody over his eyes. He flings his head back and roars down into a hole. An officer comes out and leers at Yellow Trenchcoat. He is a pretty officer—his thin tailored uniform red-clayed and tight-fitting. His pink-shaven face is girlish and his gloved hand holds a heavy .45. The Royalist colors flutter at his breast and a slim silver cane is looped to his other wrist.

"Drop that gun," Yellow Trenchcoat says dryly.

"No."

The officer is calm. Yellow Trenchcoat is calm. The bright blue erections of their gun barrels are calm. Yellow Trenchcoat fires and a nasty hole appears in the midst of the Royalist colors on the officer's chest. He lies down and dies like a gentleman. Yellow Trenchcoat bellows for a first-aid kit.

A plane whines overhead and the Captain eats his cigar and says: "Get ready for a counter-attack."

"With what?" asks Cherrynose. "I've got three rounds left."

"Use your hands. We must wait for the seventy-fives."

"Thank you, sir."

"You can skip the 'Thank you.'"

"If they skip the counter-attack."

We smile—why, I don't know—except we all admire Cherrynose—he has a sassy tongue with officers. The Captain also grins and waves a finger at him. The Captain was trade-union head before Franco came blustering out of Morocco with foreign machines and his Moors.

I feel very sick now and my stomach is in knots. I seek the cool shelter of a pine tree and Big Stomach yells.

"Here they come—and it looks as if they are silly enough to try tanks against *me* again."

Behind us a captured fascist Major is making sounds like a sick puppy.

Chapter 5

LIMBO

The seventy-fives never came—neither did the counter-attack. We lay prostrate a long time listening to the glib jargon of shellfire and the calcium glare of damage that added wrinkles to the hills in a steady barrage. There were many duds, and as night came down over tortured cypress trees, the ecstasy of war slackened and the two hill-clinging armies lowered their battle-fixed eyes and prepared for sleep. Only the sharp snap of outpost rifle-chatter cracked up out of the calm shadows of late twilight to keep us alert.

II

We are relieved at the fourteenth hour by yellow little miners who smoke big black cigars and carry the mad loose-ness of raw dynamite sticks in their belts. They bring their mascot: a reeking goat, with the red eye of a politician. With a last good-luck-to-you we are out and down the hill like tiptoeing gazelles and making for the village. Heavy dews and the low light slow us at last, as, less than fifty men that the morning dawn had seen as four hundred, we trudge along. We don't speak of the dead and missing—many times it has happened, and some cracked, crazy dawn, or some deep-draped night would find us missing and no one asking the precarious details of our passing.

But we think nothing of this now—and once on the road we break into a bawdy song led by the fingers of the Crazy Kid. We skip nimbly around the dark shapes on the road— stopping now and then to end the wild heave of smashed horses or to prop the moaning bundles of rags that beg for water, priests, or homes, by the roadside. The dead we leave alone, except for a pair of good shoes—now and then . . .

III

An hour later, I am sitting in a roofless red brick barn watching Big Stomach fricassee a stolen hen in a basin of glowing charcoal. As in his tank busting, he is calm and expert as he dips a tin spoon in the gravy, and inserts with loving care the garlic nubbins where they will do the most good. Cherrynose sits on an empty petrol tin and with the smallest pencil stub I have ever seen, is making marks on a dirty bit of paper. I close the dog-eared volume of *Morte d'Arthur* that I had picked off a red-capped staff officer we had captured in a railroad tunnel, and look up at the silly stage set of the open heavens . . . Everything is too perfect— too bright—too romantic in the big moon's unsolicited light . . . A perfect night for bombers, and we had grown to love the foggy darkness very much, ever since the enemy had been gloating over us in the sky with his Italian and German air-fleets.

Our own planes, we see too little, or not at all. They are needed over Madrid to keep the innocent enemy sport of baby killing down to a minimum. All around us the homey bustle of troops busy with the evening meal makes pleasant stirring around us.

Cherrynose puts away his letter—and I can almost quote his questions of crops and soil and dung, and the state of health of the shirtless babies on the earth floor. He pulls on his shoe-string mustache and sighs.

"It's a good year for olives. Plenty of sun and a good washing rain ought to make them this big." He holds two fingers up with enough to spare for a tennis ball.

Big Stomach wipes his bayonet on his shirt and says, as he stirs the golden torso of the hen, "I could use some olives right now—with a few strands of lettuce, some golden oil, and I'd show you a salad fit for a king."

I stir the fire with my foot and admire the sheer beauty of the hen. "A fine way for a Republican to talk. Kings."

"They ate well. What can a man do better than eat?"

Cherrynose sniffs at the corpse of the chicken, gold-brown and crackling in the pan. "Thank goodness, food is not my God."

"Fine—then Chico and I will have the breasts and you will bore yourself eating the limbs."

Suddenly from the hills there comes a fierce blast of

thunder, and sudden flashes grind fire into the face of the night.

Quickly Big Stomach hoods himself over the fire, prepared to sell his life and hen dearly. Cherrynose and I leap to our guns. We wait, breathing slowly, eying each other, saying nothing. The chicken bastes and the hot yellow skin, fatdripped, crackles in our ears like distant gun fire.

Nothing. We relax. Cherrynose looks at me and asks an opinion.

"Well, Chico—nervous farm boys firing at shadows—no?"

"I hope so—yes. I don't want to fight until we get outside that chicken. Must we wait for the war to end to eat?"

Big Stomach moans. "If this war would only end. I've lost thirty pounds in the last two months."

"From where?" I ask, inspecting the tun-shaped figure.

Big Stomach pounds his heart. "From here—poor Spain.

All these foreign dogs tramping over her with their slick heels. All these fools with their little theories and loud mouths."

I test a finger in hen grease and taste it.

"Even the enemy has no use for their allies, the prisoners tell us. More garlic."

"And where am I going to get it? I'm not in the wholesale grocery business now. Say, my wife has a secret way of cutting pockets in the chicken and then sewing in cloves. Clever woman!"

"She shows talent."

"Must you talk about wives?" snorts Cherrynose.

I laugh. "You two married men worry about your wives more than about the war. Don't you trust them?"

"Any fool can fight a war. But women are an art; an unknown art, that's the rub." Cherrynose inspects the bottles of absinthe and benedictine that he has traded for a German airman's boots (we shot him down over a field-hospital) and says softly: "My young one, some day you will have a wife and then you'll stop asking silly questions. Women aren't normal creatures. They do the damnedest things."

Big Stomach divides the steaming chicken in mess pans and wipes his mouth after a pull on the benedictine.

"There was a dark, silly-looking bull-fighter hanging around the house when I was home on leave last month. My wife says he was her cousin. *Maybe* Roman noses do belong in her family. What could I do?"

"Send for her family tree."

"Ah, Chico—I should have—and wrapped it around his neck. The dandy, with his little pigtail and his hard calves. He used scent—honest." He laughs until his big belly joins him in mirth and then the two of them laugh some more and eat chicken. I tear the sweet meat with my teeth and lick my fingers. I drink absinthe out of the bottle and it tastes

like rotting wood and I wonder where my manners have
gone. With the wind, no doubt—with the Spain I used to
love—with my two school friends that are doubled up in a
short common grave outside the Toledo Road; who died
among the dilettante staff officers on General Franco's staff,
when a plane smashed bombs down on a party they were
giving for some visiting wenches. My two poor nobles with
heads full of royal fluff.

The food sticks in my throat with my dead hopes of becoming a painter; even the sketch pad in my pack was blank,
except for the pencil note that Big Blonde had written on it
that night I bought her two bottles of pommery brut in that
twice buried-over village, under the tattered orange-brown
cork trees . . .

All she had wanted was some silk stockings and a carton
of soap. She had written this down on the sketch pad and
kissed me on the mouth. I like Big Blonde—and I try not to

think that most regiments that passed the cork-tree village did the same.

She was different from the women I had dreamed about, read about, studied in the art galleries of the continent; creatures—half fire—half milk—with minds like French philosophers and faces like Greek coins. I go back to the realism of chicken, eaten with bare fingers in a roofless barn with the landscape of unburied dead around me.

IV

Yellow Trenchcoat comes in. His face is scarred with bandages over his copper wire beard. He sniffs through his flattened nose and runs his tongue around in front of his strong yellow teeth.

"Something queer going on up ahead. Too quiet. Just keep your eyes peeled. Stealing chickens again, I see, huh?" he growled.

Big Stomach offers up a wing dipped in sauce. "My wife sent it through the post. The soul of kindness, that woman —'don't forget the handsome sergeant,' she said."

Yellow Trenchcoat tears off white meat and chews, as the sauce drips amber on his bronze beard.

"By wireless, most likely. We haven't had mail for two weeks."

I grin. "You ought to be in the hospital with your face. The nurses will get used to it."

"My innocents—there is no hospital."

"No?"

"No. There is nothing behind us but half of Spain."

"But the guns; the tanks?"

"A bluff of three batteries and a tank corps; those louse-sized ones."

"Book ends are all they are good for."

"What's up?"

"The Brass Hats expect an enemy smash through the upper hills and have moved everything—even the soup kitchens—around to mass for an attack."

Big Stomach says: "So soup kitchens are weapons now?"

"Ours could poison a division."

"We're just a shell here, and nothing covering our backsides—so keep your eyes open. They're too damn quiet out front to suit me. Those damn Moors move like Indians."

Yellow Trenchcoat drains the last drop from the pale green bottle and heaves it into a corner. He gives us a short censored salute with mock respect—sets fire to a small yellow cigarette stub and moves off to inspect and mooch food all along the line. He usually ends up with a taut stomach and a skin-full of wine. He is an old campaigner who would have waxed fat with the Children of Israel in the desert.

We sit in the squalid barn, and under the clear moon, play skat with a limp deck of cards that we know by feel—which is just as well—as the faces are almost all an oily blot—and I wonder at the lush growth of bacilli they must hold.

Far down the road a dog barks at the moon. The guttural echoes of his howls come back from the grim hills and the dog attempts to improve. Someone kicks the dog without kindness, and the night is quiet again, except for the heels of the gun mules testing their walls, and the sing-song of crickets deep in old habits . . .

We sit—three dirty unshaved soldiers, pleasurably inebriated by food and wine, deep in small talk and gastric joy. Overhead, the stars are bright and we wonder over the picked chicken bones and bottles why the enemy fliers are missing the chance of a lifetime to inoculate us with a few stingers. The cards glide; the night is gay—and we are comfortable.

The kicked dog whines in self-pity and a light wind tosses
leaves in a silky rustle over the moon-silvered earth. The
burnt ribs of the white town house are bathed in the mercy
of moon-glow and shadows, and are very dynamic composi-
tions that remind me of the Picasso Show I saw in Paris—
about three thousand years ago, counting Sundays.

V

Suddenly a figure pops in on us. Bearded, filthy with the
muck of outpost dirt, and gasping. We leap up at once—and
reach without knowing it for our rifles. The bundle stirs,
and blood, foam-flecked, comes out of the black mouth instead of words. I put out an arm but the bundle falls, and as
we bend over it, the winged buzz of bullets smashes over my
head into some shelves of bottles. The glass slivvers fly at
us; we duck. I turn quickly and Big Stomach is calmly hold-

ing his vast-covered gut in bloody hands, and then plops down on his knees. His mouth breaks into a grin and he looks at his gore-stained stomach.

"I've had my full at last."

Then he dies . . . Cherrynose grabs me and I know nothing until I am in the carnage-studded photomontage of the street, feeding clips into my magazine. I will miss Big Stomach . . .

VI

Around me is disaster as everybody loses his head in the midst of the smashing surprise. Strange troops rim the village and we wilt under their fire as we dash to seek shelter. I see the dun turbans of the Moors, the dark, red-faced Carlists and the pale fear of Italian regulars. We are almost done for. We have grouped together to return fire. Dead men and mules litter the streets and tanks, like dark ghosts, are blasting hell into the white-washed hovels. Overhead now are the air bombers—raining death in bombs and bullets, while on the flanks I hear the clop-clop of spurred horses and I think of the steel of mounted Arabs hacking at the fleeing stragglers.

A madman flashes into sight and waves bombs at the tanks. They come on steadily. Cherrynose wipes shreds of flesh from where he once had an ear, and sighs.

"Ah, for Big Stomach and his gasoline bottles. He would have loved this moment."

"Shut up."

The madman retreats, waving, and we see it is Trenchcoat with a Luger in each paw and bread-bag full of bombs.

"To the left—to the left—we've got to break through! The entire village is cut off!"

VII

We rally—not many of us—and force our way through the maddening, sobbing mass of fresh recruits, panic-mad and popeyed. Mules and men are in a wet tangle and over all, the bombers and pursuit planes make merry in our midst with explosive concoctions. I burrow through and find Yellow Trenchcoat with about a hundred men.

VIII

We follow him down a stinking alley and walk into a shearing cross fire. Men fall as if felled with a club, and grovel on the silver streets. Others lie still with their knees tight-muscled into their groins. A bloody hand begs up to me for help—but the blinding shower of a bomb grenade blows me aside and I keep going from habit only. My long coat is tailless and I have lost my hat. I move in a loggy fog.

We crouch now behind a hedge and listen to the village in its death struggle. Far off, up and down the line, there is great noise. It is a surprise attack all along the line. The front must be locked in a ten-mile struggle. Yellow Trenchcoat waves us on. Men bar the way with long rifles. We blow them aside with grenades, and the clog of our steel-nailed shoes increases their tap as we break into a run; all guns on a slant of blue-gray steel. The imbecile capers of a machine gun catch us again and we move on after some nasty bomb work and find ourselves at the edge of a wood carrying only the lightly wounded. Two columns of men—at right angles to each other—bar our way. Moors—happy, with evil promise—and pasty, short Italians. Yellow Trenchcoat pivots on his heel and rushes the Italians. A smart choice. The Italians are bad soldiers. Always we pick Italians when we have to find a weak line to break under. They fear cold steel and wilt under bombs. Their hearts are not in it . . .

IX

We break into a yell and toss in a few slotted eggs. They give way and our momentum carries us through them after a few jabs of the bayonet. I feel steel—long and saw-edged, fumble for my throat, and I look into the pretty peasant face of an Italian boy, bug-eyed with fear. I think of Leonardo da Vinci's sketch books and mash in the face with my rifle butt. Yellow Trenchcoat is cursing loudly now and I catch my wind and a few of his oaths. We turn right flank and advance through the woods in perfect skirmish order. The Italian's eyes will haunt me. We might have been fellow students. But we weren't.

Under the trees, we feel safer—but behind me I hear the snap dash of the Moors—primates gasping for the kill. We flank again and Yellow Trenchcoat throws back outposts and we line up panting behind fallen trees. The Moors come low toward the ground like hounds scenting the hare, yapping among themselves, and lit up by the pyrotechnical display of the village that is now at roasting heat and throwing fingers of flames to the heavens. But no pity sits tonight in the clouds as the bombers continue on their stints. Our round rapid fire catches the Moors off guard.

We roll up the flank and rear of the Moors and blast away. They are not Italians. They turn and fight and we finish them off with the grenades. A tall, hawk-faced Moor worries his knife through a comrade and then slits off his ears. We get him twice through the back and when we see the bloody skins in his paws, two men grab him and nail him to a tree with bayonets. I turn, feeling puckering in my throat and follow Yellow Trenchcoat down a woodland trail parallel with the now red-hot burning village. There are too few of us left.

X

A slim lad, struggling under a long gun, trips over a creeper and I give him a hand. He steadies himself and we go on beating the woods like beaters. We run into machine guns again and the slim youth goes down. I yell.

"Hit?"

"No—no, of course not."

"Come on—you'll get left here alone."

"I hope not."

I help him up and I see that his trench coat is too big for him. In the flickering light he looks very young. Yellow Trenchcoat is cursing a blue blaze at the men we are facing. They are our own machine guns. We have run into our rear guard. We march in over the outposts and find ourselves in a mad panic of walloping whirling men. Everything is in an uproar, guns at all angles, order fled, and all men after it.

Officers try to rally their men—but nothing avails—not even shooting—the din is head-aching. Wounded pass on comrades' shoulders, dead or dying get the ditch with a callous push. Equipment clatters down on all sides.

XI

Screaming horses wade into us and swing past the mobbed roads pulling batteries, the drivers are mere whipping-machines as wheels snap limbs like pipe stems. All run with open mouths and the panting Red Cross men fight to find space to attend to the wounded. A large Rolls Royce—with a silver lady still flaunting her drapes on the radiator, blocks a road. We push it farther off the road and find a staff officer asleep in the back. We can't awaken him—because someone has blown the back of his head off. He looks as important as ever. The panic grows and the weaker are stepped under by panting men. Everyone must follow the stream and we all look back too often.

Behind us, the village is settling into a glowing bed of embers—like the fire we used to roast potatoes in—in another world. The enemy is beyond us on the right and going fast to encircle us.

More and more machine guns, blankets, gasless cars go into the ditches. Many throw away guns, belts and even water bottles. Many are now running fast—running faster. Most of them collapse and we pass them looking up to us with their tongues hanging out and blood pouring from their nostrils.

XII

A man shoots himself and bungles the job; a friend has to finish him off. An officer tries to stop a group from climb-

ing on a gun carriage. They stab him down and he disappears under foot. I step high to avoid him—but my heel
sinks into something. More wheels come behind. I try not
to think of anything. Good soldiers don't.

I can't move. We all mill down the road and scream to
those ahead, who do the same. I am wedged in. I can't move
and I fight for space and push about with my bloody rifle
butt. I hear a gasp and the slim lad I rescued in the wood

is going down in a whirl of men. I grab his shoulder, and
tearing, and pulling, I get him erect. Cherrynose is pounding
into broad backs for space and Yellow Trenchcoat has
reached a new high level in oaths with which he sprays both
us and the enemy alike—sometimes he adds his Maker.

"Damn you civilian dogs. Open up. If the planes ever
sight us, we'll all go on one bomb."

"Break rank!"

"Don't bunch in targets!"

"Spread to the fields!"

XIII

Nothing helps. I put an arm under the slim youth and hold him to me. A man goes mad and begins to mount on his companion's back. Others follow the red eye of panic and the ditches fill with guns; with a growing collection of bombs, food and entrenching tools. Many shed their greatcoats and drop blankets as they run. A jam fills a crossroad and many jabber and scream, while overhead the planes come low and spray human flesh into threads with their machine guns. The last guns come through, the riders beating their horses until their pink nostrils flare open and shut with agony, and their white-yellow eyes roll with mad jerks of their heads . . .

XIV

A six-inch gun is herded through, and then follow the Red Cross flivvers, brimming full. The road packs up again and we are stuck.

Madmen flay their friends with red steel for elbow room —and the dead toss in the ditches under the steel hobs of their rank-and-file mates. Magenta bombs are everywhere, blooming suddenly underfoot into huge red roses of pain and acid.

Yellow Trenchcoat sees all is not well. He opens his vast mouth and roars. He slaps us to the side of the macabre road.

"To the hills, you scuts. Break rank!"

Few hear. I grab the youth and we leave and tumble over the thorns. We run, we pant and my shirt is wet against me. My torso burns. I stop and pant. We are alone. The youth sobs unashamed. I pat his arm. Far off I can still hear men die. I look at the youth. He sinks down and I pull him to his feet. We must be far by morning. Far. I am a fool to burden myself like this with a comrade. Old soldiers travel light and alone during a retreat.

XV

Together we go on—on into the night until nothing is heard behind us—but we both know that many men are dead and that we two are walking away from our unused graves. Until next time.

That's how panic comes, that's how an army breaks up, that's how retreats happen. Maybe I missed a lot, a lot the literary people will look for and not find. But writing it out this is the way it was to us. We were there.

Book Two

NONE BUT
THE LONELY HEART

Chapter 6

BUEN VIAJE

L<small>ATER</small> *they said the break through had been stopped with weary troops under heavy eyelids, and even Chico felt maybe it wasn't too bad. He drank almond* horchata *with his Captain and didn't talk much about the losses and asked for leave to go to Madrid to see some friends. On the mountains the stale shabby snow looked unfashionable for Spring . . .*

"Buen viaje," *said the Captain, and three days later Chico stood in the Atocha Station at Madrid and wondered why the natives called it "Mediodia." Very high up a Savoia Marchetti and a Heinkel sat in the sky, but the afternoon bombing had not yet started so the articulate sound of the city buzzed every place . . .*

A CITY CALLED MADRID

NO PASARAN! MADRID SERA LA TUMBA DEL FASCISMO!

said the flapping red rags all along the Gran Avenida de la Libertad, and there was a church burning on the Gran Via, where, a porter told me, some monks had been caught sniping from the bell tower and, like all *Madrileños* I met, he spit in the roadway and shrugged his shoulders, feeling you couldn't do much or expect anything from those black crows

95

. . . There was a sense of full morning, a frequent hunt for sun at street corners.

II

The shelling had filled the streets with stones and broken bricks and somewhere a house had been burned out and a few women (Madonnas of the Bombs) mashed under it. But the Domenico Theotocopuli, and Ribera and Zurbaran

and Goya paintings at the Prado had been taken to safety. A few shell holes, like mad eyes, were visible in the skyscraper of the Telephone building, and I smiled at the idea of a lot of Republican-American dividend holders who were going to be left holding the bag. It was good to be out of the lines and going to see Shad Roe and Annabelle (and if I was a good boy, she had written, she would let me play her gramophone), and in the square where *autos-da-fe* used to fry and roast Spanish people while the Bishops looked on, the men in blue overalls and their fat girls and dark little tarts and

pregnant wives were standing in line in half-abstracted com-
mentary to see Dooglaz (Douglas Fairbanks) and Carlito
(Charlie Chaplin) in a theatre with the Gonzogas' motto
Nec spe, nec metu . . . neither with hope nor with fear.

III

The only hotel with running hot water (three hours a
day) was very full of big-name journalists, but Shad Roe
took me to the owner, a worried little oily man with only
one ear lobe, who said he would throw some Hollywood
people out of a room and take me in—and Shad Roe took
me to the bar and we drank a good brandy and rested against
the bar and listened to the richly clad war "experts" in polished boots win the war for either side and I thought of
psychoanalysts' love of excrement . . .

"Jesus," said Shad Roe, "you look like a wooden Christ
on a peasant church wall."

"I'm all right. Good to see you."

"I thought they did you in up there."

"Almost. How is Annabelle?"

"I wouldn't know. She's very busy showing famous Americans—all lovers of hemispheres, curved lines and fannies
—the war."

"Everybody feels pretty sure in Madrid."

"They'll win, they think," said Shad Roe.

"No," I said. "They can't."

"Don't say it so loud. We live here in a fusion of glory,
acid and nostalgic odors."

"It's all over, Shad Roe. We fight with almost nothing.
They have guns, tanks, Messerschmitts, Piaggios, Junkers.
They have plenty of everything . . ."

"What's the matter with America? *This* is a fellow Republic."

A fat man at our elbow laughed. "Ha ha. America. The Harvard frumps in the State Department are almost all for Franco . . . Every college kid that comes over here to fight is scratched off the lists as a citizen and called a Red. What's a Red, mother?"

Shad Roe said with a smoky, luminous look, "Go away, Hank—you're drunk. A Red, to reactionary Americans, is anybody who says democracy and liberty is worth fighting for—anyone who says it's either us or the fascists some day, a struggle to the death, and if we don't help Spain now it will be harder for us later. A Red, my dear Hank, is a sonofabitch who tells anybody who has made his pile or smashed unions that a great world revolt of the have and have-nots is coming. Lindbergh, Ford, Pegler, and Sumner Welles are not Reds."

Hank, a cameraman and a damn good one as I remembered, said: "And I used to think a Red was a dope who liked Karl Marx."

"Who is Karl Marx?" asked Shad Roe stiffly, the old school tie suddenly running up.

"You think this is the beginning," I asked, "of the smashing of world democracy?"

"It's all over," said Shad Roe. "England and France are lost, and you Americans are blind and daffy with too much flush plumbing, cinemas, and have lost the values that once were fought for at Gettysburg."

Hank leaned against the bar. "We Yankees are all right. It ain't our fight—let the huns and spicks and limeys cut each other's necks. The Ou Ess Ay is good enough just as she is, brother. Boy, I'd like to see a broad cross Times Square against the lights again—her shafts against the neon orange-drink signs and the taxi horns knocking your ears off every step you take. No one will ever attack that or us."

"Where can I find Annabelle?" I said. (How long ago

this all was.) "This talk doesn't mean anything to me. I'm going into the line in three days."

"Sucker," said Hank with a faint enigmatic smile. "What's it to you, chum?"

"Not a damn thing. Maybe Franco is the boy to back. Maybe Hitler and Hoover will lie down together some day in the same bed. Where is Annabelle?"

"Try that dance jernt," said Hank, lipping into his beer, ". . . where they dance the *seguidilla* and *jota* and Roseland fox-trots. She hangs out there with some Yale boys in crew haircuts over here with the Red Cross."

Shad Roe looked at me, started to say something, waved me off as if he objected to me—and never deviated into too human an intimacy. He went back to his drink.

IV

A lot of happy little American girl reporters in neat, tailored pants and Fifth Avenue breasts came in as a band started fat, gloating indigo music, and I went out and bought a newspaper from a *gitanos* gypsy and near the *matadero,* that foul slaughter house where cows died like ants, someone fired a machine gun with that fragmentary, inchoate bark the guns have.

V

People passed and I picked up some shell fragment marked *Roma* from the curb and I wondered if I should mail it to Washington, but what the hell—I felt too good to worry about world politics and the decay of the fellow democratic spirit. Real belief in anything seems to adhere mostly to the past.

Men passed with two prisoners, their hands tied behind their backs. They looked like fairies, and kept spitting at

everyone and the dirty, barefooted kids yelled *Oles* as they
passed. Someone said they had been found planting bombs
under a water pipe. Near the El Retiro a lot of little soldiers
with very happy tarts, their thighs enough to make a bullock
jealous, passed me, a joy to see as they held on to their
girls and couldn't get them fast enough into the shrubbery
of the park; and around the corner from the Bajada Ae
Metro Station, two honeymooners—he in blue overalls and
a bullet belt, and she in dark silk and a huge comb—were
having their picture taken against a painted backdrop of the
Empire State Building (which looked as badly rented as
ever). The park had a humid spermy hay odor and the
golden pollinated day grew sunnier.

VI

A long line of wounded men were being hauled by old
trucks across the Toledo Bridge—a stink of rotting flesh and

bile came from them and only the kids and old women stopped to look at them—men whose eyes, mouths, were mere pained slits drilled and slashed in red meat.

VII

The shelling started at three and I had to duck into a cheese shop's dark glow and an old hag leered at me and asked how young I liked them and would I care for a virgin —very rare these days. Reckless, foolish soldiers wasted valuable property as if it were *barquillos* wafers and as cheap. I said, no thanks and she said it was safe—the girl's father was *el gran capitán*—her own son, and with Franco— and soon he would be back and shoot all these lousy (*mala*) workers—and from between her withered breasts, she pulled a huge brass cross and began to curse all *Madrileños* who didn't pay for their rancid cheese.

I went out into the shelling to escape the cheesy fascist witch and it was very heavy shelling. It did no very great damage to morale as far as I could see. But Franco didn't mind. He had a lot of Nazi shells and guns and could keep it up for a long time. Hurt horses passed with haggard, uncomprehending eyes.

VIII

I didn't find Annabelle, so I went back to the hotel when the shelling stopped and found my mouse-nest and lay down and fell asleep on a bed stuffed with small stones and slept a long time, until someone chased a girl on high heels loudly down the hall and she ran screaming and laughing past my door.

"You are a card, Joe," she howled in Vassar English. "Just a great big card." And then I just looked up at the ceiling, listening to someone on the floor below playing a gramophone recording of *St. James Infirmary*. The door opened and Annabelle came in and kissed me. I sat up. She looked very good in blue overall pants and a white rabbit jacket very short in back and rope sandals on her stockingless feet. I had a nicely qualified basis toward her.

"You look lousy, Chico."

"I don't feel bad. What is this hotel—an annex to the Astor Bar or the Algonquin Round Table?"

"Except for Alec Woollcott, everybody is here. Hemingway is at a party—you must come."

I looked around the room, held together by layers of old wallpaper.

"No—I'm going back into the line—and I'm moving out tonight."

"Where can I find you, Chico?"

"It will be over soon—this war. See you in Paris if I can make it."

She grinned as banging campaniles started in the city. "The Dome—third table from the left—where the *bella grassa* sits—blonde, plump and overripe."

She went out and I got out my razor and looked in the mirror and began to lather my face. Someone was throwing big iron balls against the hotel. The gramophone was playing again—*Summertime*. It didn't seem so bad to have a republic die to a Gershwin tune. . . .

THE END NEARS

At that time the Republic still held together, but Chico knew and all the little men in blue overalls under great wreathed sycamores in battered villages knew that it wasn't going to be victory. "The American State Department, the British industrial groups, the pressure of the Jockey Club and the Two Hundred Families of France had done their work well," Yellow Trenchcoat said to Chico.

"Better get to the border—it's all over soon."

"I'll stay. We've got one good fight left."

"Sure—maybe one good one."

And the next day with the desperate clatter of steel and bronze tools they crossed the Ebro and saw the radiant plains beyond Escatron...

YOU CAN ONLY DIE TWICE

All week with insatiate military greed there had been fighting up and down the brass-colored river and the bodies of the dead rolled in the sun-washed waters, and the living waited in their fox-holes suspended in time and memory, waiting for the Nazi planes to go away. The officers carefully saw to our arms and gave some of us permission to go to a town right behind the lines to see a *fiesta de los toros*. It wasn't much of a bullfight. The cape play was bad and the horses' *malgas* opened up and sewed together too often and the bull a little too small. There was only one bull. When Spain is down to one bull, you can bet things are pretty low for the Republic.

But it was good sitting in the sun—the guns booming ten miles away and the little black bull dunging in rage as he tried to catch an oily youth working very *cenido* (close) with a red rag. His short *verónicas* were bad and his *camboi* and *rodillazo* passes lousy.

II

Then the great shelling started—there must have been miles of German guns wheel to wheel across the hills—and after it stopped we moved up into the lines and just waited, a sensual sliding around our hearts. Whatever it was, we could see it wasn't going to be neat and sweet and fragrant. And there was no chance any more to make for the border and save my pelt. Some integrity still held us soldiers . . .

We were approaching a big battle and the whole front rocked with the excitement of a first night opening. All along the line, the mighty pitch of preparations was going on. Night and day, the heavy fields echoed the pounding wheels of the supply trucks and the snaky hiss of marching infantry in long weaving columns of bayonet-topped lines.

Under a hot sun the men marched beneath hunchbacked burdens, and passed up the heat-hazed road toward the sputter of continual gunfire that rimmed us in. The dun dust of grinding, clinking machinery passing us caused no more comment than a herd of sheep.

III

At night the heavy artillery came up with much swearing, and cases of long evil shells, packed in lemon-yellow straw,

lay everywhere. Red Cross flags broke out like poppies in
the fields and at all hours the planes droned overhead and
dipped their wings in greeting to us.

Officers came with miles of wires trailing behind them
and rubbed heads over many diminutive maps. The rains
came too—but the slick wet sides of the machines went on.
The roads were ankle deep in the taffy-colored mud and
dead horses and mules floated in bloated ease over the
many ruts. Men came until the land could hold no more.
Still the business of war went on.

Even we were pampered, polished, rearmed, shod and
overfed—so that we knew that soon the mighty red haze of
battle would come down on us, a hood of sinister promise.
We knew the whys of it—but took what we could get.

The men wrote last, gay letters home, and moved metal
mirrors over their hearts. Some used packs of cards—and one
secretly used a Bible. The veterans pinned slips of paper
bearing their names onto their tunics and we then saw that
this was all very serious. We spent all we had and borrowed
from all who would lend.

IV

All night it rains and when we get up from our straw
pallets, it is still raining. The spotted, lead sky drips down
in solid sheets of water, and as we sit eating cold stew, we
watch the heavy cars plow up big, splashing columns of
mud in the road. The mad, eager toss of the gun horses—
their eyes and nostrils big with fright, tell us that something
is up. Animals know. We line up and wait as the rain comes
down through our collars and our toes wrinkle in our soggy
shoes.

There is an extra measure of sour wine and then we are
packed into trucks that grunt off into the sticky mud. We

bounce around and shove at each other with damp distaste.

It rains.

We sit and get wet.

We stand and get wet; some even lie down and get wet.

We ride until noon and we creak off and flex the twisted muscles and make small silly jokes among ourselves. Cherry-nose drains water off his face and sighs.

"It's good for the soil. How the cabbages must be grow-ing, and the wheat must be this high. I hope the wife planted everything."

Yellow Trenchcoat, deep in dirty white muffler, walks up and down the line inspecting the guns and bellowing.

"All right, leave your heavy packs here. Three days' light marching equipment."

"That means extra shells."

"Fat chance we have to eat from now on."

"No wine rations up here."

Yellow Trenchcoat eyes the men and grunts.

"All right now, men. We're moving in twenty minutes. Our objective is the yellow fort. Keep going until we reach it. Remember we must keep contact with the men on our left and right. Any questions? Intelligent ones?"

There are a few. They get barked answers. The Captain and Yellow Trenchcoat set their watches. We stand and wait and squirm under the rain. I am calm and think of nothing—or almost nothing.

We swear big, ringing oaths, as the light tanks pass, splashing mud. Big ones follow, slower, clumsier and bearing one-pounders. Never have I seen so much equipment, so many big shells, such hurry and bustle and so much infantry.

A few men light gaspers and keep them under the dripping rims of their tin hats. One fat man eats jam out of a tin and gets his face messed up like a baby.

Suddenly, behind and ahead of us, big guns take over. The world spins sideways and slips in space. Our barrage keeps up the ear-shattering din for twenty minutes. The very ground jumps about and trees snap and shake.

Flocks of airplanes fly over, and we see bombers, pursuits and observation ships dart toward the front, their motors sounding like big nasty bees.

Hell itself reigns on the front. It is blue fire—with pure yellow or red bursts. We are the second wave and we wait for the first wave to have earned their daily bread. Someone faints down the line and is pushed toward the bushes.

I think suddenly of my life. Perhaps the man fainting brought it all back. I don't know. One doesn't try and think too much. There is killing to be done.

We are moving forward. Where is the first wave of attack? We say nothing—just wait. The first wave must be all dead by now. First waves never have much luck, but they don't have to wait around and fidget.

A whistle sounds in silly piping peeps and we duck our heads low and push rain out of our eyes. Suddenly we all break into loose order and move forward in slow time, arms all on one slant . . .

The men are tense and watch the fields with great care. There is nothing to see—only the wet golden wheat—the blue-green sheen of wet trees and the shell-tormented sky, colored like the inside of a teapot.

V

We come now to signs of battle—the first tanks stalled in mud—the few overturned staff cars, showing elegant cord tires high in the air, and the usual drifting deserters—green-faced and panting, who swim past us in the rain and move toward the back as our officers threaten them with Mausers.

A shell wails overhead—we bend and wait. It explodes into a bloom of red flames and three men go with it into the air . . .

Dead men now float under foot and one red-bearded officer lies on his back and from his stomach a long, unwound white bandage floats in the mud. The big guns pound on and when we pass them, trotting in the spray, the crews yell at us and keep banging in the shells. Large nude men man them in blinding flames.

VI

War has come now to the land in real earnest. The wounded die harder here and one tank has been a direct hit. A whole field is planted with dead men facing forward and we gag as we splash past a first-aid station in the open air under a sad, wet, flapping flag. Some neat soul is piling the wounded into rows like a lumber yard. A sleepy doctor in pink rubber gloves watches us pass.

VII

The front lines appear; shallow mud holes full of cadavers waiting to be covered with top soil. Ahead are patches

of barbwire piled into pointed hills. We slide past them and now we open our mouths and pant as we gingerly pick our way among the first wave. The rain makes them look alive as it plays on their faces. Their limbs dance in the downpour. All around me, men are falling down with surprise on their faces. I go on, head low and wait for death. We cross the hill and machine guns reap among us. Half of us go on and we pass the spot where the armies met in full career. The ground is piled with tanks and shells and guns and belts of bullets. Grenades are under foot and strands of barbwire are twisted into neat designs. The bodies of men are over everything like an even dusting of pepper and salt. Wounds on them splash bright colored . . .

VIII

Few of us are left and we kneel down in the mud and wait. So far we have seen no enemy—only his fire has met us and, as we are blood and flesh and bone, it has damaged us a great deal. We are too weak to go on. Young recruits lie screaming in the filth—but no one pays them any attention. We lie in the wet, red dirt and wait while the whining burst of steel flies over us.

Our flanks have also stopped and under the curtain of fire we lie and listen to the slugs grunt into flesh, or the snap of shell fragments as they nose into screaming men. Cherrynose drinks with a bobbing throat out of a canteen and hands it to me with firm flat fingers.

I gasp a guzzle of it and sputter. It is raw, new brandy. I turn and hand it back and shake my head.

"I'll take shell fire next time."

Cherrynose refuses the canteen and his big dark eyes watch me tenderly.

"Keep it."

"I've got one full of water."

"Keep it anyway. Something to remember an old friend by."

I grin and then stop. Cherrynose is holding his chest together with a fan spread of fingers. He makes a bad job of it and I see that it has a red-frayed look—like a slipper chewed by a puppy. Machine gun bullets have sawed him in half.

"Chico. I'm dead."

And when I reach his side, he is. I sniff, and quickly transfer his papers to my pockets. Somewhere there is a cheerful little Spanish farm and a dirty floor full of little naked babies and their flushed, plump, barefooted mother. I surprise myself by producing a tear . . .

IX

Yellow Trenchcoat is yelling into a field phone, calling some general names. I *know* the general is not on the other end. He hangs up with a bang and throws the phone away.

"We go forward with the third wave. All of us."

"Not all of us. Cherrynose stays here."

"Lucky bastard—we'll get ours in that reeking swamp ahead. I'd much rather die up here."

I duck back into line. I feel that I have a spot reserved in that swamp.

The third wave comes up breathing hard through their muddy faces. They pass and we melt into their ranks. All the world is in flames and we stumble as we pass a burning building, smoking in the rain. Two haystacks burn like gutted candles alongside . . .

Machine guns catch us here and we cough and go down and wait (those that still live) while some sergeants with ease bomb the nest flat into the ground and wave us on.

X

We move between burning houses and try not to step on the things that the artillery wagons have passed over. A big bomber has been brought down on the outskirts of the town and two neatly tailored airmen lie beside the ship in strange broken poses like snapped dolls. They have yellow hair and square skulls.

A soldier steps out of line and removes their shoulder tabs. The grind of tanks sounds ahead and we pass a whole group of them mixed with armored cars. They are our escort and we fall in between them to wait for the fourth wave to reach us. A few shell-torn groups of the three waves are left and with wild rolling eyes, they wonder why they were fools enough to escape alive—when the next wave will carry them to certain death, anyway.

XI

The fourth wave comes—stepping with smart nervousness. They are shock troops with automatic rifles and machine guns on wheels. For fifty miles along the front, there is a moment's lull and now with a simple arm wave, we move on.

We see the yellow fort between the popcorn of shell fire. It is deep in barbwire, and hidden guns spurt fire in our very faces from it. A flag hangs, red, gold, and wet in the rain.

We are all running now between the armored cars and tanks. Overhead, we are covered by our planes until a heavy, black group of crows comes up from behind the yellow fort and begins to take pot shots at us. A dogfight develops and we leave the planes behind.

XII

We run, open-mouthed—yelling something none of us hears and pant stronger every time a man near us is chopped down. We are all running so fast now, that the dead tumble in somersaults after us before they fall and lie still.

Some of the wounded refuse to fall and stagger and spurt along with us.

I trip and smash my head against a tank. I put out my hands and push myself erect. I stagger as the tank rumbles on in a reeking puff of gas. I begin to fall—but someone grabs me and I grin up into the singed copper beard of Yellow Trenchcoat.

"Steady," his lips say—but I hear nothing. We finish Cherrynose's canteen of brandy and with a small fire burning in our stomachs we go on, stepping very high over the fallen. Many men are down and the tanks are all alone now in front. The armored cars are mostly all disabled and the shell fire steadily grows stronger.

We are sorry with self-pity as we look around us.

A man wanders past, holding himself together and sadly calling:

"First aid—first aid, *please!*"

A tall thin man bangs his head against the ground as if pounding out a headache. He lies down, pants, and I see a bullet hole between his eyes. He stares around and begins to pound his head into the ground again. I want to tell him he can't be alive—not with a bullet between the eyes—but think better of it. It may kill him knowing it is there . . .

XIII

Suddenly we all spring to our feet as if shot up from strong springs. No one has given any orders—but I have seen this strange thing happen before in other battles. During a lull, the men would spring up from all parts of the field at one time and run forward. Just something that can't be explained.

We are nothing human any more. We are the ghosts of the four waves of the attack. Nothing can kill us now and the fools who fall dead all around us are sacrificing their lives needlessly. We know that nothing can kill us—they wouldn't die either if *they* knew it.

We are running very fast now. My knees come high and fall back fast. I can feel the jar as my heels tear into the turf and bite out chunks of soil and grass. Over us, the yellow fort looms and the tanks can go no farther into the pits and wire jungles.

We throw away our guns and tear up the slopes throwing hand grenades as we go. Egg after egg, we throw ahead of us.

Outposts—gun nests—pickets melt away like a bad dream before our expertly placed bombs. We no longer walk or run—but float a few feet above the ground and with calm deliberate ease, throw in our slotted eggs. We feel nothing.

XIV

A few of the enemy rise to meet us with cold steel and we duck under and throw. They disappear like a fairy-book mist. We are on the dusty lip leading to the fort. A few of our tanks have found a road and they move ahead of us with a tinny rattle. Men pass us now, fingering cold steel and probing bodies with their bayonets. The waves are rallying now and we dash on and beat them to the fort lawn.

Dust, flame-colored, puffs out of the fort windows and there is a mighty crash of glass and plaster and falling beams

from inside. Dead men lie around shamelessly and we hunt the living out of dark corners . . .

The environment takes on the acid smoke of battle and more and more tanks and armored cars find paths to the fort and join in the braying around the dry moat.

They close in like a pack at a fox hole and pump scarlet flames into it with an even, steady roar. A group of men comes forward with hands high and we close in and shove them down the hill. Someone yells something and we see a white rag fluttering out of a window, held by a thin, dirty wrist . . .

XV

More men stagger forth and then come the wounded, very tender and wide-eyed, holding their shattered members close. We stand and pant as a group of officers comes out from the battered face of the fort and then we go in with great care and bayonet the furniture.

Some men come in and set up new wires and then a staff group, smoking black cigars, marches in and becomes very talkative over large scale maps and slap each other on the back. The switchboard begins to flash in colored lights and men speak with great detail into many phones.

A few dead men ignore the staff and we stand around until the sergeants begin to roar at us. Then we drift around the fort looking for food. I find a loaf of white bread and feed myself in big doughy lumps. I can hardly swallow—but hunger knots my stomach, so I force the white bread down.

Yellow Trenchcoat comes toward me sweating with might, and rubbing his flat nose.

"Chico, take five men and guard the wire-laying detail that's going out to splice in General Headquarters."

"They picked a fine time for it."

"Yes—they want to catch the afternoon papers with this story."

Outside, it is still raining . . .

THE FARMER

"It was a battle?" asked the old man at the crossroads. "Yes."

"You have been very careless."

"Battles are like that."

"You have trampled my wheat."

"We are sorry, old man."

"Damn your sorry, and your 'old man'! I am a farmer."

"It's good land you have here."

"It used to be mine. Now it's the bank's."

"There is no bank, old man."

"Nonsense. There may be no God as the young men say . . . but there will always be a bank."

"You are a foolish old man."

"A fool maybe . . . but no 'old man'! I'm only sixty-two."

Chapter 7

AND NOW IT IS OVER

IT WAS a moment when time passed and space waited and maybe it was a few months, maybe weeks, but it was all over or just started bigger elsewhere, and I had gotten away in time. Just a few of us did . . . too few . . . and the Spanish earth was rotting with good men dead, and the Franco boys were killing everything they could find in many drunken military courts.

I had papers—false papers, true—but I could get away with them. And in one dirty town where men and beasts had lived together a long time and left their marks, and marked their leavings along the bottoms of walls, Moors and fascists were shooting a lot of barefooted Spaniards, tying them to posts, standing them up on broken feet, looking at watches and giving the order to fire every twenty seconds. It was not good to watch . . .

II

On the train through France, I suddenly wanted again books—lots of books. I could do without men for a while. And all I had was Ben Jonson's version of some of Petronius Arbiter (stolen from a villa that bore the arms of the Duke of Alba—but *not* from the Duke, for he was waiting out the war in London, at the Ritz, while the English ladies gave him parties) . . .

But that was not enough to read, and I made a list of books new and old that had fed or spoiled my world . . .

Hitler's *Mein Kampf*, Freud's *Interpretation of Dreams*, William James' *Varieties of Religious Experience*, Shaw's *Man and Superman*, Spengler's *The Decline of the West*,

William Graham Sumner's *Folkways*, Veblen's *Theory of the Leisure Class*, Bergson's *Creative Evolution*, Frazer's *Golden Bough*, Tolstoy's *What is Art?*, Joyce's *Ulysses*, *The Education of Henry Adams* and John Dewey's *Democracy and Education*, Henry James' *Golden Bowl* and Lenin's *Imperialism; the State and Revolution*.

ENGLAND

"Oranges and lemons say the bells of St. Clements" and to Chico they said a lot of things besides; that he was free,

*that he was alive, that he was clean, that he was out of uni-
form, that Spain was dead—a great, festering grave—and
that he needed a job . . .*

*In front of the Law Courts a newsboy of fifty, with Mons
medals on his fallen chest, stood groggy from his resurrection from frowsy sleep, a banner in his dirty paw:*

PEACE IN OUR TIME
CHAMBERLAIN FLIES TO MUNICH

"Piper, sir? All habout hit!"

*"No thanks," said Chico lighting a cigarette with a twinge
of compunction. "Have a gasper?"*

*"Don't mind ha bit if I do. Piper, piper! All habout
hit . . . !"*

MUNICH *DANSE MACABRE*

So there were the bells of St. Clement Danes and the far-
off dome of St. Paul's floating in the soot-filled London air,
and I was a fool going up Fleet Street hunting a newspaper
office and Shad Roe, and perhaps the promise of a job. The
city of London sat in a stupor waiting for the umbrella man
to dust off his knees and come home from Munich with his
tail up—stout fella—and that seraphic expression seen on
constipated sheep dogs.

II

I found Shad Roe as I always found him—between drinks
—or about to begin a bottle. He sat at a desk fit for the
British Museum, and the decorum of an English newspaper
office tiptoed around him.

"Hello, Chico. Bum show?" said Shad Roe, benignantly
smiling.

"I got out alive. Your turn next."

"You think Chamberlain will fight? That eighteen-jewel Empire-movement bastard?"

"What else can he do? He can't sell out the Czechs."

"Don't talk rot here. Let's go have a snort. *Homo sum et nihil humanum a me alienum puto.*"

"I want a job. Not a reading from Terence."

"Not a chance—American and all that."

"We have English reporters in New York."

The wire service box in the corner began to twitch. A report by Major Eliot:

As a matter of cold fact, the Germans are far less ready for war than they were in 1914, they lack the resources for a struggle of any duration, their Italian ally is the weakest and most vulnerable in Europe, their economic and financial situation is uncertain (to say the least) and their armed forces are suffering the pains of rebirth begun only four years ago.

Men stopped rattling their tea cups and stood very still. A dirty boy came running past us trailing a fluttering ribbon smeared with ink and it was suddenly very still along the Victoria Embankment—as if everyone between Westminster Bridge and Blackfriars were holding their breath—almost as if they had stopped counting pound notes at the Bank of England and the Royal Exchange, as if the buses had stopped stinking up Trafalgar Square and the Mall going past Nelson's statue and the National Gallery and the Church of St. Martin-in-the-Field—as if every damned Covent Garden basket balancer had stopped and just stood there, his mouth open in ugliness and inadequacy, waiting for the word of hope and wisdom . . .

III

I have never felt anything like it in any city before or since, as when the British Isles and the city of London suddenly felt that icy feeling around its heart, knew that some defective incompetent had failed to live up to his old slogans, past heroics.

IV

Shad Roe grabbed the inky boy.

"What's up, you cove?"

"Hit's done. 'E's done it."

A large man built like a bulldog, with an indecent nakedness of baldness, looked at his foul briar pipe. "He's sold out the Czechs."

Shad Roe hunted his desk, tossed out an old shirt and found a quart of pinch bottle. "I expected it. Business as usual. Carry on, steel-mongers, and Lady Cliveden of Astor. Let's drink to the sadness of a goal achieved."

We held paper cups of whiskey in our hands and Shad
Roe looked into his and spoke in semicolons.

"To Chamberlain; always late, always wrong; the last
dragging umbrella on the merry-go-round before the great
explosion; gents, *ce n'est qu'une bagatelle.*"

We drank—editors, copy boys, some ink-stained wretches
from the engraving hells.

Bulldog said: "What does it mean?"

Shad Roe poured again; he had an odd saurian quality of
voice. "The Empire—it's finished—cooked and served with
Munich sauce. What happens now? What survives, if it
does, will be something else; but not the old school tie and
the furled umbrella—they are dead as old secret tantric
teachings. Let us get out a special edition and get drunk."

Bulldog stared at paper ribbons coming in over the tele-
type. "Do you think we ought to get out a special?"

"The Empire falls, the Church of England's solemnization of matrimony totters—and you wonder if you should wait for the cricket finals!"

A phone tinkled in the polite British manner and Bulldog picked it up. He made sounds into it and set it down as if wounded in his susceptibilities.

"*That* was the Brass Hat."

Shad Roe tossed away the empty bottle. "And what did our honorable publisher want?"

"Play down the Czech angle . . . and give everything we have along the line of Peace in Our Time . . ."

"Come on, Chico," Shad Roe said, "let's get out of here. I don't own a million shares of Vickers the way the Brass Hat does. Let us, like Candide, say: '*Il faut cultiver notre jardin*'—or a pub."

V

The people in the street knew. They stood very still and looked at one another. We went to a lot of pubs, rode and walked and had more pubs to visit, but the dreadful emphatic tattering of British pride was always there.

At last Shad Roe brought me to an ugly square marble thing. It was the Cenotaph at Whitehall to the Empire's war dead. Rancid and rotting flowers leaned against it. On either side the War Office and Colonial Office stood. Tall thin men (like English motion picture actors in Hollywood) walked along the curb toward their offices. It was wonderful the control they showed. They took their time, wore neat uniforms or good tailoring.

Shad Roe looked at the stale flowers, the ugly marble shape with a sympathetic scrutiny.

"Well, we've done it. We've uprooted and broken any hope of an Eastern front. The Czechs can fight Hitler but they can't fight Hitler, France *and* England, too. This smashes the military hopes of Europe. The Russians are right not to trust us."

"Why did they do it?"

"The dying and the old, Chico, like to leave as much damage behind them as they can. They hate the living and the young. Chamberlain so ends a life and martyrdom of extraneous legendary lies."

"That's no sane answer."

"There will be no sane answers for a long time. Let's have dinner."

VI

O England full of sin, but more of sloth!
Spit out thy phlegm and fill thy breast with glory.
Thy gentry bleats, as if thy native cloth
Transfused a sheepishness into thy story;
  Not that they all are so, but that the most
  Are gone to grass and in the pasture lost . . .

"Did you read that in the piper, ducky?" said the bar maid.

Shad Roe shivered. "No one reads Herbert any more. Our poets pick their noses in Mayfair and write sonnets to my lady's drawers in *Vogue*."

"Shall we eat?" I asked. The pub was filling up. Dock workers, smelling of the rank salt of sweat, stood around with pints of bitters; and *their* love of poetry wasn't written on their face. Shad Roe was in a state I had never seen him in before. He lifted his gin to his mouth, drank, and rolled his eyes . . .

'Will you remember what Defoe said:
Thus from a mixture of all kinds began
That heterogeneous thing, an Englishman:
In eager rapes and furious lust begot
Between a painted Briton and a Scot . . .

The royal refugees our breed restores
With foreign courtiers and with foreign whores,
And carefully re-peoples us again,
Throughout the lazy, long, lascivious reign,
With such a blest and true-born English fry
As much illustrates our nobility . . .
Six bastard dukes survive his luscious reign. . . .' "

"We'll 'ave no talk of bastards or 'ores 'ere," said the bar maid.

"Bastards or not," said the dock worker, "that's the truth. The bloody truth. It hain't every gent what will tell it, sir . . ."

'We have offended, Oh, my countrymen,
We have offended very grievously,
And been most tyrannous . . .
A groan of accusation pierces Heaven . . .' "

And with the last line of Coleridge rattling in his throat, Shad Roe turned a strange green and fell into the sawdust on the floor. For the first time in his life, Shad Roe was dead drunk. Chamberlain had performed another, bigger miracle . . .

"Hain't 'e the little reciter now," said the bar maid handing me his hat . . .

TOTTENHAM COURT LIFE

I have two friends who live in one of the mews off Tottenham Court Road, where the rents are not very high and the talk not as smart as in Mayfair. And I wanted to forget Chamberlain for a while—and Shad Roe, who was too full of drinks to talk any more and the Nazis were massing in the headlines . . .

Grace and Joe got married in Paris and went back to London because they never could become great artists anyway. I knew them at the little cafés at the Place du Tertre, and when I hit London I looked them up and we drank a lot of local wine and talked about Thomas Benton with dislike, and Goya with respect. Joe was out of work and Grace was looking for a place that needed a telephone girl. I stayed the night at their place and dreamed of Daumier and the Sacre-Coeur above Montmartre.

II

The sun is pushing past the eccentric color of the yellow drapes, exposing the usual cramped two-room Tottenham Court apartment that is part of every rebuilt house that advertises in the *For Rent* section of the Fleet Street papers. Under a high, dirt-stencilled skylight of whitewash and dove droppings, there is a huge, carved black table covered with big catafalque-designed lamps shaped like Queen Victoria that were so popular in the better undertaker parlors twenty years ago. The table also plays host to picture frames full of writers, actors and cartoonists, and the revolting spectacle of a tacky, unwashed tea-set in which someone had tried to serve a complete spaghetti dinner. I am lying on the sofa— a corner that is forever England—wondering if Joe and Grace are up yet. A sofa spring stabs at my left kidney and a train whistles at Waterloo Station . . .

Doors lead to a bathroom and to a hall exit. Against the back wall of the little bedroom off the living studio room are two wall beds, the kind that drop out of a closet (except when they stick and break fingernails). They are shambling (I saw them last night) repellent objects in their unmade state, and they take up too much space. Joe and Grace still fill them.

III

To the right of a rocking chair from the hire-and-purchase shop is the studio sofa, draped in some fool's idea of fabric designing. I lie on it. Over it brood reproductions of modern painting. There is a smell of gas, face powder, wet umbrellas and Joe's shilling pipe tobacco, and a raincoat *not* from Savile Row.

A large trunk stands open under a large view of Fujiyama in full colors. (It looks like Fujiyama, anyway.) Parts of a marimba orchestra are tacked to the walls in arty groups and over a gas cooking grill there is a hanging bookcase full of Faith Baldwin, Thomas Wolfe, Alexander Woollcott and three gift copies of *Gone with the Wind,* as well as a small radio set giving off morning BBC music since I pinched it alive. The wallpaper is holding on to the walls as tight as it can but its grip is slipping now that Chamberlain has failed. I feel very happy and I know Joe and Grace are happy and it's because we all remember our artist days and now we are older and it's good to see each other and I wonder about all the people we once knew so well in that school where they taught us that art and advertising were going to save the world for Bruce Barton and Coolidge and Harrods and Bovril . . .

I stare at ceiling murals painted by water pipe drippings; the ceiling is rain-spotted also, and bugs have been happy there. Joe and Grace stir in their bedroom.

There is even a small, streaky-colored dog called Tea Rag —a live, yapping little powder-puff with bangs in his eyes, who is calmly breaking his fast on a shoe—my shoe. I doze off again. England is at peace and I remember Shad Roe saying *Aequam memento rebus in arduis servare mentem— guard the calm of your soul even if your affairs go astray.* Horace, of course, like most of Shad Roe's Latin . . .

IV

From the bathroom there is a great splashing of water and the interesting sight—rear view—of the ogival architecture of a lush, titian-haired girl (Grace) who is brushing her teeth with the proper up and down motion so much advocated by the better dentists. She is following through with her whole limber body. Wet stockings and panties hang around her. I remember Grace in Paris drinking *bocks* at corner *zincs,* and the years flip by too fast.

On one of the wall beds lies a spread-eagle sleeper in a cerise coat and pants, styled like a combination cassock and surplice. The sleeper is Joe, a little fatter and with hair missing, but a damn fine fellow, the kind of Englishman I like, admire, and drink with. His English earth is a small box garden on the windowsill.

Still brushing her teeth, Grace comes out of the bathroom, drops three eggs into the coffee pot bubbling on the gas ring, turns as the phone rings in the bedroom and goes and picks it up.

"Who? Just a minute."

She turns and with a slippered toe she stirs Joe. I watch him moan through the open door.

"Wake up, Joe. The employment agency near Old Bailey."

Joe stirs, comes suddenly alive, brushes his face free from sleep.

"Oh! Oh—*them chaps* . . ."

"A job maybe."

Joe is at the phone, breathing with excitement.

"This is Joe. Yes. Yes. I can pop over. Right away. Thank you!"

Joe hangs up the phone and reaches for a handful of clothing.

"It's a job with some advertising layout department. Three of us going up. I hope I get it! Do I stand a show?"

"I hope so," says Grace. "It's been a jolly long time for you between jobs."

I wink at Joe and read the want ads.

STENOGRAPHER for large real estate management office; must have held similar position, must be accurate and speedy; only those stating qualifications, names of last employers, religion and salary expected will receive consideration. Box 2 *Times*.

STENOGRAPHER-TYPIST, experienced in accounting office; reply stating experience, age, religion, salary expected. A 755 *Fleet St. Annex*.

V

The employment agencies from Hyde Park to the Elephant and Castle are packed. Huge files are filled and Grace explains it to me. Pens scratch out details of lost jobs, new hopes. Girls, women, virgins, wives, mothers, tramps, ladies, college girls, taxi dancers—there are thousands of them. Grace is a damn good window designer. *Not today, dearie.*

In hall bedrooms, in railroad flats over pubs, in dreadful mail-order suburban villas, in clubs and hotels they read the Help Wants, go tired and foot-hot to the agencies, make penitential journeys on Old London buses, fighting strenuously with elbows, wonder if they should study airplane welding or wear the old school boater.

Grace and Joe don't worry about a car they haven't got. The coming war booms, the big money in shipbuilding, the fat contracts, the big stuff Vickers is paying dividends on, it's nothing to Grace and Joe. They want a job to keep the two-room flat, the shoe-eating dog, the two folding beds, the man-killing sofa and maybe a night of Shakespeare at the Odeon.

At noon I buy Grace a big lunch and then we go on hunting.

Shabby, smooth, classy, nifty, hungry, pimply girls; Colonels' daughters, cockney baggages, pub maids, lovely, cock-eyed and buck-toothed; cover ads, underwear models, peaches, tarts, houseworkers, nursemaids, bookkeepers—willing, worried, hungry as hell, Katherine Mansfield characters, widows, tired, out of bus fare. Maybe airplane welding *is* the answer. (But the school is a bit of a gyp, they say.)

VI

Tonight we celebrate. Joe has a job. He is going to get three pounds ten a week in the drafting department of a tank factory. It's good pay. The factory is only making three hundred percent on its investment of Col. Blimp's money. But Joe is happy to serve his nation. Joe has only a hell of a desire to work and keep Grace happy and the little dog fed and the greengrocer paid and a few pints of bitters under his belt.

I order wine.

"Remember," says Joe, "the night we gave that art party at the *Café des Deux Magots* . . . the night Jack went to New York?"

"Sure," I said, refilling the glasses. "Grace was engaged to that rich Egyptian wop. Wholesale fruit. *Don't pincha de grape—pincha de cocoanut.*"

Grace grinned. "He was slimy with money and I wanted to get Joe mad."

"I got mad."

"You broke his thumb on the sidewalk—in front of the Gare de Lyon. Remember when you sold your first drawing to *The Passing Show?* . . . And whatever became of Larry?"

"Larry? Larry? . . . Oh, he's around—doing fine on Long Island, selling *Collier's, Satevepost.* Got six kids . . . all cartoonists."

"What do you know—proper family man and all that. Well, I've got to get up early for the job tomorrow. Be an M.B. any day now."

Grace kissed me good-bye and gave me a Saint Anthony in a white metal capsule. What wonderful people I know.

VII

But I wasn't happy in England; the kiss of death puckered over it, nothing got any better and the Nazis got a little worse. Nobody talked any more about Peace in Our Time. Everyone hoped they would be able to hold off the Nazis— keep them away from the island—now that they had smashed any hope of holding them busy in the East with the help of the Czechs (—and soon now there would be no Czechs). Some bright Eton boys had the idea of getting the U.S.S.R. to fight the Nazis.

It was a game of dog eat dog but the last little scheme stuck in my gullet—although Shad Roe said there was nothing wrong in the idea *except* that Moscow wasn't having any.

Shad Roe was buying sun helmets and little pills for tropical ills ("keep your bowels open and your fly closed in Asia, Chico boy"), for he felt any day now he would be off in a cloud of glory reporting another big war and he wasn't going to be caught in the tropics like most British generals of fame and song, "with nothing between them and the damp ground but a thin native girl . . . *ha ha!* . . ." I laughed, too and we drank a last martini, very dry, and shook hands and I went to see about going to France. Annabelle was in Paris. I wanted to get away from the sight of the East India docks loading steel and tools for Bremen and Yokohama and Naples so as not to disappoint the stockholders. And Lady Astor was giving a big dinner for the Nazi von Ribbentrop's pals and the House of Lords chopped logic like liver and committed tiny adulteries. . . .

BEEF

"Don't you fear," said the cabbie. "We ain't licked yet. There is plenty of beef in us lads yet. We ain't all edjitcated frumps full of wind. You siy to anyone you meet . . . *we'll fight* . . . !"

Chapter 8

OF THINGS PAST

Once, *like an expanding crystal of emotions, he had been very young in Paris, and very happy there with a puppy's idea of happiness. Now Chico was going back and perhaps everything he had once liked and been full of illusions for would be there again. He would take Annabelle to the Chez Larue and they would say a lot of foolish happy things. Who knows?*

*And then he got off the train and in the streets the Came-
lots du Roi were rioting and shouting* vive le Roi—dictateur!
*—rich, fat louts they were and he wondered if Maxime Wey-
gand was still behind them. Then he remembered old Cle-
menceau saying:* "Weygand must have had a lot of kicks in
the behind when he was little."

And he thought of sole Joinville, *duck* Perigueux *and a
sherbet* l'Ermitage *going down Annabelle's lovely throat. . . .*

LAND OF THE *DEUX CENT* FAMILIES

"Oh," said Annabelle while the mobs were singing the
Internationale and the *Carmagnole* in the streets. "I'm married, you know."

"No," I said, looking at the Moët and Chandon in wet
linen shrouds, labeled '21. "No, I didn't know."

"I'm married to the sweetest little Frenchman you ever
saw. Remember Charles Boyer?"

"You should be very happy with him."

"Don't be an ass. Mine just *looks* like him. He's a *maître
de requêtes*—a solicitor-general—and maybe soon a *chef-du-
cabinet* . . ."

"It sounds fine."

"It is fine for me. No more kicking around in border inns.
No more acting like a lady tramp in half a dozen international newspaper offices. Good-bye recurrences of funny old
refrains. I'm going to have a dozen babies and end up a fearful French hag with kids in the Lycée Charlemagne and the
École Normale Supérieure. You'll see. There's more to me
than jasmine perfume and good legs."

"I'm seeing now. You sound very happy."

"I'm pregnant. How is Shad Roe?"

"Fine. Not a sober moment—and the Latin flowing like
brown October ale. He drinks that, too."

"Isn't the world wonderful, Chico?"

"No," I said. "Don't you feel all hell about to break out?"

"No. I see things on a higher, calmer plane now. News-paper people are daffy." She lit a Grises Gitane. "Nicotine might be bad for the unborn heir." Heir of the Banque of France, Banques Hottingeur Mallet, Lazare Frères, de Wendel (steel), de Vogue (chemical stinks and poisons), Timardon (industry) and Darbley (paper and newsprint). It seemed that Annabelle's husband was connected with all of them. "So you see, Chico—I've got to be careful of the kid's health."

"But don't you see all those things are selling out the French Republic, the people in the street, in the fields, the things the French Revolution was fought for?"

"How silly."

"Look. I know the bank-church-army-business group is forming fascist organizations to sell out to Hitler."

Annabelle looked at me. "Honey, you *are* morbid. Don't you know I'm a fascist?"

"Are you? You were there in Madrid with the Loyalists. Hell, you saw Franco's butchers at work killing women and kids. What's come over you?"

"Love. I'm so goddamn happy, so pregnant. I'd sell my soul, like Faust, just to stay this way."

"Hitler is not going to let you and your new friends keep their happiness, or lie tranquilly in their soft beds."

"That foolish little man is no match for my husband."

"I'd be willing to bet against you there—sight unseen."

She looked at me and smiled and took my hand. "It was fun in Madrid, and fun at Capri, and fun in London. But that's all over for little Annabelle. I'm settling down, and all that stuff about republics and democracy and liberty is all right when you don't care where your next meal or dress is coming from. But you'll see—it will be better this way."

"I like you, Annabelle—maybe the only fascist I can ever say that to. But I can't agree with you."

"What are you going to do?"

I signalled the waiter. "I am going to try and hate you."

"Before you do, let's go to the art galleries. And there are some rare books on display I want to see. My husband collects English first editions, you know."

I helped her up. "He's got a rare item in you. . . ."

II

The rare books were near the Luxembourg, and Annabelle got Spike, a hairy poet we both knew, to help us look at the books. Spike wrote huge epics and published light verse and had a wild red beard and thought all good writing—except his own—had died with Tolstoy.

Spike had one other bad fault besides going berserk in his cups. He hated collectors of old books.

"Next to postage stamps," he said to us, "the most foolish collector, the biggest fool and nastiest of human beings I have met is the man whose main purpose in life is to collect old and dirty books because they are rare and because they increase in value—not because they are well written. Show me a collector of first and rare editions and I will show you a man with something nasty in his make-up."

"Dear me," said Annabelle.

"Fortunately," Spike said, "I'm not rich enough to be in the nasty class. But most rich book collectors are. They would not give a living author a cold cup of coffee—and would see a good writer starve (I know several doing it right now, if you want to know) than buy his books and put them away for posterity. But let some writer of rare trash, some scabby item become scarce—and, baby, in go these ghouls to collect and save and lie and fake and cheat and hoard until you would not think all they hug is a dirty, badly printed book so full of germs that it should be burned in public and the collector whipped in the city square as a menace to good health. Collectors are all *malin*."

III

I don't always agree with Spike. We found the rare book place. Rentiers sat in the park. Paris rested. An auction of rare books was on. Little, dirty books, I admit, that you can buy in good clean reprints for fifty cents. There was a poet's item—a cheap little pamphlet of some of the early Poe poems. It sold for thirty-six thousand dollars to a director of Schneider et Cie., the big French gun plant. Annabelle knew him.

Spike said: "Poe died of hunger, neglect and despair. Not one of these well-fed dogs from Creusot, Comité des Forges, these bearded scum-collectors bidding today would have given him a dollar for a meal. Look at them gloat over that soiled paper rag. Walt Whitman once stood on a curb begging—saying: 'Will you spare a dollar, mister, to keep a great poet from starving?' "

The dealer's helper, a fruity boy with eyeglasses on a ribbon, came over to us bowing and washing his hands without water; a perfect product of the Lycée Henri IV.

"Ah, have you seen the Gutenberg Bible? J. P. Morgan bought one just like it for a hundred thousand in American dollars."

"Did he ever read it?" asked Spike, pulling on his beard and building himself a hand-rolled cigarette.

The Frump showed his perfect store teeth and pulled on his eyeglass ribbon. "Read it? What for? It's a collector's item. We have his *Morte d'Arthur* printed by William Caxton. Brought forty-five thousand American dollars from Mr. Morgan. Are you gentlemen bidding on it?"

"I read it in high school version," Annabelle said. "I remember it pretty well. Dull and corny."

The Frump looked at me and then stepped back for a better glance.

"We have a complete modern catalog. Of course we are experimenting with living Americans. *Toujours joyeux.* Frankly," he made a sound like a happy horse, "you living boys don't—as they say in the cinema argot—*pay off. Un peu exalté* (a little bit nuts) for our trade yet."

Spike was hunting through a list. "How many first folio Shakespeares are you knocking down today?"

"Oh, my dear *sir!* There are only two hundred first Folios. The Folger Library has eighty-two. Mr. Folger was president of Le Standard Oil, you know, and he hunted for years for the William Jaggard copy presented by the publisher to a friend. It's uncut, you know, and has the original engraving of W. S. by Droeshout."

"W. S.?" asked Spike of Annabelle.

"William Shakespeare," said the Frump.

We nodded and looked at the Frump and he went to a case and came out with a dirty little account book. The sort of thing the butchers used when I was a boy to charge the three pounds of soup meat I used to carry home twice a week.

Annabelle sniffed it. "Must be *pretty* rare! Smells like a dust bin."

"Oh, it is. It's a Stratford diary and contains this interesting item. 'Shakespear Drayton and Ben Jonson had a merrie meeting and it seems drank too hard for Shakespear died of a feavour there contracted. . . .'"

"Interesting *if* true," said Spike.

The Frump hugged the gamey book bound in dirty *horizon bleu* to his thin chest. "It's priceless."

"Oh, come now . . ." said Annabelle.

"It's not for sale, anyway—just for exhibit."

IV

There was calm talk up front and the gouty collectors held their heads together, bit the ends of fresh cigars and began to watch their agents bid. After a while someone stood up and said something and new books came up and then two large old men with neat gray hair, Legion of Honor ribbons, and watch chains very thin across vast guts stood up and began to hammer each other over the heads with canes. Very pleasant sounds resulted. Like dray horses walking on the huge *pavés de Flandres*—that grand road.

Men separated them and, snarling in a low key, their vests unbuttoned, they were drawn apart and stood cooling off in corners while men fanned them with linen handkerchiefs scented with musk.

"*En avant, soldats chrétiens,*" sang Spike.

The Frump bit off a fingernail and plucked at his eyeglass ribbon and came over to us shaking his head.

"Dreadful—two of our best rare book dealers. Each worth millions—sheer *American* millions—and acting like schoolboys over a red apple. The German one bids for Goering."

"What was the prize?" asked Spike.

The Frump went holy with awe. "Charles Dickens, *Christmas Carol.* One of the original manuscripts he sent to Chapman and Hall, his printers, in 1843. Even an earlier one than the Morgan manuscript. Such a cheerful, healthy story, full of cockney patois—I always thought. So full of kindness toward mankind—so full of calmer understanding between people, don't you think?"

There was a shout and the two lovers of Dickens were again locked in battle throwing words at each other. Spike, Annabelle and I got up and went out. The last sight I had of the kindly millionaire rare book dealers (in American dollars) was their locked limbs wonderfully strangling each other—(a lovely sight for a living two dollar and fifty cent author) and the Frump hissing: *"Merci bien!"*

V

Annabelle went home in a Renault only a block long and hung with a coat of arms worthy of being on a cigarette package. Spike and I found a place to have some *fines* and I said:

"Think of Annabelle—her being pregnant and turning fascist."

Spike nodded, slumped into a lower attitude, and tugged at his beard. "The pregnant part is a surprise."

"You bastard," I said, "still being the flip bright man,

aren't you?—the enigma—acting like something out of Aldous Huxley. . . ."

Spike grinned and rattled the saucers at his elbow. "Don't
go long-hair, Chico. There are no practical enigmas any
more. A woman is only as intelligent as her bed partner. If
Annabelle had married a fried-fish man from the Flea Market, she'd be rooting for the *Cartel des Gauches* and all
power to the sit-down strikers . . ."

"France looks bad to me, Spike. Everybody buttering his
nest and nobody giving a damn about saving a damn fine
civilization."

"Civilizations *always* fall apart at their peak. I'm going to
Italy to live."

"Well, you don't have to worry about a peak of civilization in Italy. Only a fat man with no ass for destiny."

Spike did not answer.

"What's the matter?" I asked.

"Nothing. Only if I have to live under a head man, I'd rather not do it under the coming goon—that slimy spider, Laval; *Le Bougnat* . . . that coal and wood thief of Auvergne . . . *malin,* wet, oily as hell, a *couloir* politico. No, I'm going to Italy."

"Why not come home to America?"

"I don't believe in America any more. It belongs to Ford and du Pont and the oil crooks and the Irish fat-bellies who have seized political power. When it belongs again to the people who killed the buffaloes and built cabins and hunted for long rivers . . . But, no. No America for me."

VI

Well, there it was. Two good friends gone over—and their reasons sounded too soaked in soft leisure and mirror love.

I said: "You are going to Italy and Annabelle is thinking of future generations of Frenchmen. Why?"

The poet grinned and showed his broken teeth:

"Beasts do the same 'tis true, but ancient fame
Says gods themselves turned beasts to do the same.
The Thunderer who, without the female bed,
Could goddesses bring forth from out his head,
Chose rather mortals this way to create,
So much more he esteemed his pleasure 'bove his state . . ."

"That's all Europe means to you?" I asked.

"That's all. Ever read Marlowe any more? He knew his Europe:

"My men like satyrs, grazing on the lawns,
Shall with their goat-feet dance the antic hay . . .

There you might see the gods in sundry shapes
Committing heady riots, incest, rapes;
For know that underneath this radiant floor
Was Danae's statue in a brazen tower;
Jove stealing from his sister's bed
To dally with Idalian Ganymede
And for his love, Europa, bellowing loud . . ."

"Poetry isn't enough, Spike."

"There is only poetry left—worth living for—maybe not even that."

"What's it all going to lead to?"

"Who cares . . . ?"

"What will it leave behind it?"

"You really want to know?"

"I do," I said . . .

"The drunkard now supinely snores,
His load of ale sweats through his pores;
Yet when he wakes, the swine shall find
A crapula remains behind . . ."

VII

A crapula and a baby—and that's how two very good friends saw Europe, and perhaps the world. And the people in the streets who were not as brilliant or as beautiful as my friends . . . what did they see?

I could either write this down just the way it happened, or I could skip it, and I didn't want to skip it. I wanted to know and find out, and Spike, sitting there scowling—a great poet, I thought, yet lost—maybe forever—and then the waiter breathed into my ear and we had some more saucers put at our elbows and we went away to eat smoked turkey in a purée of chestnuts. And some recherché delicatessen that, Spike said, over a dripping beard, was truffled wood-cock, snipe and sour tamarisks.

Anyway, we and the French could still eat, and every place that night we saw them sitting as near the white tablecloths as they could get with their fine broad bellies, eating the wonderful food, drinking the gay wine, sucking their very fingers with pleasure and grinding delicate flavoring be-tween thick yellow teeth, while some place, near the river, searchlights made a half-tired attempt to practice air-raid drills, and in the street the *Camelots du Roi* marched with minds as big as the maraschino cherries in our Old Fash-ioneds.

A beggar came up to us and Spike told him, scram, you beggar, in impeccable French, and the Nazi ambassador passed on his way to the Ritz where the beautiful Greek and Italian tarts with red hair walked in sensuous loping strides to hear important men talk of the states of their livers or bank accounts. It was like an *entr'acte* before the headliners appeared . . .

I said good-bye to Spike and he went away rubbing his beard and muttering in Greek or D. H. Lawrence—and I never saw him again. At my hotel there was a radio mes-sage from Shad Roe. He was going to Germany to see about the great Nazi rearming and he could take me along to help carry his portable typewriter. Would I be at the Gare de Lyon? I would.

I called Annabelle to say good-bye but she had gone with her Charles Boyer type over to a Nazi-French cultural din-ner for better understanding among the two nations' indus-tries.

At the station the newspaper "experts" said the French Army was the best in the world. Goebbels from Berlin had first sent out *that* report . . .

SMUGGLER

"They caught a smuggler," said the German train conductor.

"What was he smuggling in?"

"Nail polish. Pink nail polish."

"That's not very criminal."

"Hitler made it a crime."

"That makes it official."

"To be sure . . . but my wife doesn't like it."

"No?"

"This Hitler is a great man. My wife is afraid of him."

"I see."

"She was never afraid of anything . . . not even the devil . . ."

Chapter 9

ROMANCE AWAITS YOU IN GERMANY (Travel Poster)

I*T* WAS *just after Lord Rothermere—a trifle infirm—and his pro-Nazi reporter had admitted everything looked pretty good in Germany, that Shad Roe and Chico arrived at the Friedrichstrasse Bahnhof and walked down past a phalanx of snooty Nazis (standing stiff and repulsive) waiting for somebody important.*

"For us?" asked Chico with a feeling of disintegration.
"Hotel Continental," said Shad Roe to the taxi driver.
"This glamour, my boy, is for Lord and Lady Runciman
who have been politely packing up the Czechs for Hitler ..."
"Oh ..."

And in the book-store windows the best sellers were Vom
Winde Verweht *by Margaret Mitchell and* Der Totale Krieg
by General Ludendorff ...

THE LAND OF THE CARPET EATER

As in all *Deutscher hofs,* the Continental staff were spies
on the side, and we found our hand baggage well picked
apart and replaced almost the way we had left it. The night
clerk, however, was very kind to us and he said we were
not to fear, as nothing under an English lord interested the
teppichfresser—the carpet eater.

"Why *teppichfresser?*" asked Shad Roe in a ghastly travesty of a leer brought on by the night before drinking.

"He *eats* them when he gets in a rage. It impresses Englishmen."

Shad Roe nodded. "Imagine it would ..."

And, as we went out, the framed carpet lover in an old
gabardine trench coat, hung over the desk looking down at
us with a mouth full of soiled teeth. In the street a lot of
young boys with shovels were marched—a full *Spechchor*—
chanting chorus—singing something delightful about blood
sprouting from their knives; howling hoarsely in the chill
air.

II

We were looking for a Baroness. Shad Roe knew her and
she sold things. Things like information to newspapermen,
and she had a studio flat in the Tauenzienstrasse. But she

preferred to swank at the Adlon where a smart girl with the right kind of breasts and eyes could do herself the most good with the Wilhelmstrasse mob. We went to the Adlon.

"The Baroness is all right," said Shad Roe, stopping at the bar near the door. "You *must* be understanding."

"I will be."

"Tolerant."

"Of course."

"Live and let live. Berlin is a ghastly travesty on life."

"Sure."

"Her husband was a little Budapest swine who sold out to Hitler, and left her to starve when he went to South America for the Lufthansa who are trying to get air bases near your jolly old Panama Canal."

"Rubbish," I said, and we finished our drink and in the sky heavy bombers were coming over from the direction of Tempelhof Airdrome. At the Adlon there was always a *stammtisch*—reserved table—for newspapermen and we acted important and sat down and ordered beer and read the Swiss paper *Baseler Nachrichten* which was better than the kept press. The headwaiter, a Nazi careerist with squinting flexible features, went to see if the Baroness was at the other bar, and Shad Roe waved to someone he called Lord Londonderry, a pro-Nazi—but who looked English, I said. Shad Roe said he was.

"So!" I asked.

"So what? Didn't Lindbergh pilot the Nazi plane—the *von Hindenburg*—for the Hitler crowd and give his impression of it to them? Just a little *service,* that's all."

"Well . . . maybe . . ."

The waiter was back and told us the Baroness was at Habels and so we went there, and I remembered the table where Tom Wolfe used to sit and eat three or four meals at a time and drink beer and Pfalzer wine and talk about how he was lonely, and was going to die, and wanted a girl ... And later he wrote a lot of books on those themes, and it got a little boring to read them ... but he was a very fine writer—only he never got over his subject matter of being lonely, mortal and sexual. He missed greater widths of time and space. ...

III

The Baroness was sitting at the bar and I loved her at once. She was huge and blonde, like a Rubens painting come to life. Very beautiful, strong, with long shapely legs and a little black mole at one corner of her red-larded mouth, and a huge fox pelt was tossed over one nude shoulder. For some reason she was still in evening clothes. She had a clear, healthy complexion and a tuned brusque voice.

"Shad Roe!"

She kissed him and he kissed her and they ordered a huge

artillery barrage of Martinis. And I met her and she held my hand and I loved her even more. She was crisp, clear and very alive and very intent on life and very much full of a zest that poured from every cunning bulge of her tight silver gown.

"How charming, how charming," she said, kissing me, too. "American? He has *that* too much money look."

Shad Roe swallowed a Martini. "Where in Hades were you? We need help."

She smiled and the sun shook as if it reflected in her Martini glass. "Of course. I'm a girl that loves money. I can get you anything in Germany—or Poland—or Austria—and maybe in England. I was with Lord Lothian's party last night."

I groaned. "Are there *any* English upperclass people who aren't in Germany *or* love it?"

The Baroness smiled again. "I love that foolish umbrella man—what was his name? Superior to his class—inferior to his habits . . . ?"

Shad Roe growled. "You know goddamn well—Chamberlain."

"Ah, yes . . . Chamberlain. He was worthless to me. So chaste and in full use of his honor. But he gave us Austria and soon he will give us the Czechs—toss us the Czechs—even if they are not his to give. You English . . . !"

"We want to see the German Army," I said.

"How sweet he is," she said, patting my head. *"He* wants to see the German Army. The age of reason is lost when Americans kiss their first girl."

"Can you get us a permit?" said Shad Roe.

"A poor girl has to think of her old age. It *could* be done —but it will cost so many of your nice English pounds."

"I'm not rich," said Shad Roe, lifting a filled glass.

"Your paper is. The army press-chief is meeting a girl

I know at the big Gedachtniskirche—funny place to meet a girl, in a church—but he does, and he can get me permits to see the Army maneuvers. Call me in two days. I get results. I envy American women the divorce, and the privileges of lawful incomes."

"And the cost?"

"*Wie, bitte?*" she said in mild cynicism.

"All right, we'll pay," said Shad Roe, patting her rump. A newsboy passed shouting an extra about *Polnischen Grossenwahns*—Polish madness—and Shad Roe said, "So that's the way the wind blows . . . ?"

The Baroness looked over the people in the place. "Have you noticed how German women lack ankles? I'm Hungarian myself, you know."

"So, after the Czechs—the Poles, maybe?"

"Twenty pounds may get you an answer. Want it?"

"*Abgelehnt.* My paper doesn't want to stir that up."

"Kiss me then and go away," said the Baroness. "I've some things to do. Be at my flat tonight. I'm giving a party for a dear friend."

IV

So we kissed her on the cool smooth cheek and we went away and I said:

"She's really out of spy fiction. You invented her."

"Oh, no," said Shad Roe, borrowing a light from the corner *schupo*, "she is very much *not* selling glamour or tight black-silk-clad flesh." He thanked the cop and we went on. "The Baroness is just a business girl selling anything a newspaperman might want. Rumor, facts, documents. She has reliable infatuations for the right people. I met her last year through Lady Astor. She got me a pass to the Sportspalast when the head Airedale was speaking."

"Isn't all that dangerous?"

"Nonsense. Life *isn't* like a Hitchcock cinema, Chico. There are a lot of Nazis who like a little extra spending money and she peddles their stuff for them. Her protection is perfect. Frankly, I think she works for the Gestapo and they let this small gossip stuff go on because she is so wonderful at her work. But don't think she is a romantic, or a Mata Hari. The Baroness is just piling up a lot of money for her old age—in American bonds, I might add. She admires America—and Americans, you lucky stiff."

V

A long line of people were standing in front of a store trying to buy underwear, and Shad Roe got out his notebook and wrote something in it. He smiled. "I have a lot of little items. 'Everyone is going to get food cards soon and I hear that horses, pigs and cows and chickens *not* living on farms will each have to have their own personal food cards. . . .'"

"That's just English humor. . . ."

"No. Shows you how unfunny and efficient the Germans are."

"Any other items?"

"The Papal Nuncio is said to be in Berlin peddling soft smiles; there is skating at the Tiergarten; a *hausfrau* has been arrested for calling sugarless, fatless pudding *Hitler's Quatsch;* and the rumor is that the army maneuvers near Kulmbach are really an invasion army ready to take over all of Czechoslovakia—not just the Sudetenland."

"Where do you get these items?"

"Not from beautiful Baronesses . . . their prices are too high for ordinary gossip—or is it *more* than gossip?"

"I think it is only gossip. There is too much gossip."

Shad Roe looked about him for a bar. "Son, the veneer of Christian civilization, never too thick on this damned German race, is flaking off. Behind these fat, red grunting faces, there is no moral lard—no pains or scruples behind all these cold, greedy eyes . . ."

"I don't see it," I said. "They are people just like other people."

"*Homo homini lupus* . . . man is a quarrelsome animal," said Shad Roe.

THE OLD LADY SHOWS HER TEETH

I dreamed that night of an old woman I knew in London. She sold very wilted flowers outside a small pub.

"Care for some flirs . . . sir?"

"No thank you."

"Bitter cold, hain't it?"

"Very . . . aren't you out late tonight?"

"Hits them blasted hairraid drills we been 'aving down hour wiy . . ."

"They expect bombers."

"A fine time to wake a body . . . middle of last night . . . 'ootin like thiy was tikin ya to Blackpool for a bit of black-puddin and gin."

"Was it a good drill?"

"Ai, that it was."

"Everything go all right?"

"Ai, that it did. Me Joe, hup 'e is at the first blast . . . and runnin down the 'all his breeks flappin round his bum . . . 'owling ya'd think ole 'Itler 'imself was after him. ' 'Urry, 'urry' he 'owls at me . . . 'Koomin' I siy . . . 'just wanta git me teeth off the shelf . . .' ' 'Urry,' 'e 'owls, 'and blast yer damn teeth . . . 'Itler ain't going to send no sandwitches . . .' "

"He's a witty man, your Joe."

She smiled showing huge yellow teeth, regular as paving blocks. " 'Urry, 'e 'owls, 'and damn yer teeth . . . 'Itler ain't going to send no sandwitches . . .' "

I woke up to hear the Nazi planes flying over Berlin, and it was still a lovely morning . . .

Chapter 10

HITLER IN THE FIELD

THIS *is* an army such as Field Marshal Paul Ludwig Hans von Beneckendorff and von Hindenburg never dreamed of. It walks the hills, it rides great, eight-wheeled carts, it struts in gold and black under gore-red banners marked with crooked crosses, it stands in the dust while Der Führer passes, surrounded by his guards who herd the precious, nasty thing he is. All the new concrete roads are packed with thousands of trucks and in each truck sit twelve men—each in a coal-bucket hat, armed with a new rifle, shod in heavy leather boots, carrying his kit and himself into mock battle under tough *Obergruppenfuehrers.*

II

Across the cropped wheat fields the stink of oil and the rattle of steel comes from thousands of tanks, each *panzer-kraftwagen* following in order the one before him, like heavy black elephants on parade—but, unlike elephants, (as each one passes the little man whose mad, cunning brain thought of all this) each one belches skyward its iron entrails, sends out every shell and slug it can spare—even the twenty-five ton tanks carrying the 40 mm. guns.

III

By the brook where bees once navigated floral rapes, the engineers lay—thousands of them—stripped to their brown hips; and soon they leap up and set in place large Erector toys that become bridges and great tractor-drawn 8-inch mortars and guns pulled fast, rattle over them. In a vast field, concrete pillboxes, like evil mushrooms, blossom out

and then *lustknabes* from Mars, wearing tanks of fire, approach them and burn them out and the tanks come over them and sit on them hard and everyone applauds. Maybe because this time there was no one in the pillboxes . . . Huge men, shock troops appear.

IV

And overhead the planes are heavy and dark, against a crayon-blue sky and they never stop coming—Heinkel K bombers which are very big. Now they are not the same

planes coming over again and again because they fly off to
the East and keep flying and different kinds of planes take
their place—Messerschmitt 110's. There is something called
a Stuka diver and there are huge three- and four-engined
bombers—Focke-Wulf Kuriers; and there are slim, nasty
looking fighters shaped like dragon flies; and all keep at a
certain height and keep moving.

Last come Junker transports full of troops. And the roads
are packed and the fields are packed and the little man standing proudly, madly, in the field; his shiny boots, his little
Iron Cross feebly strangling his swelling neck, are covered
with a light dust. And yet I am sure no one gives a damn
outside of Germany about this army—nor do they take seriously the talk of *Endkampf gegen England* . . .

THE MAD MARVEL

There is no doubt too much written about the little man
of the porous nose undulated upward, who looks like a
music hall comic, acts like a case history out of Jung, and
will destroy more of civilization than Napoleon, Attila, Ford,
Caesar, the Rockefellers, or the Moors of old. But I suppose
some dangling posterity will want to know what I saw and
thought of him in that storm of dust and steel and marching
German flesh.

II

He stands twenty feet away from me, tramping down
larkspur, balsam and clover. He stands strutting (a thing he
can do better than anyone I've ever seen). A sort of "at
ease" position, his hands clasped in front of him, the way
dead Crusaders are sometimes carved over their tombs—yet
strutting at ease, his fierce weak face transformed into a
happy leer of satisfaction, and he *is* happy.

It bubbles from him, this sinister happiness of his, this mad happiness (for he has the maddest eye in Christendom and the most cunning). A band plays *Lohengrin* music as fat as Goering. His belly digs a little against his pants' top, the neat, plain jacket is beginning to stain under the armpits and his *Wehrmacht* cap, like a baby cobra's hood, looks a little silly over his burlesque comic of a face. The amazing thing is when he turns around and you see that there is no back to his head—none at all. It fits in with his lobed, fat-bridged snoot—and the jaws of a large foetus.

III

Actually, of course, he is too simple. If you have read your abnormal case histories, you have him—a brilliant, unstable madman with a voice and a soft, moist, languorous mouth. It is a remarkable, harsh voice, it is a thoroughly German voice, and, I suppose, the proper voice to inflame half-wits, and the German race seems to be run by a gang of looters, simon-pure bums, in power over a race of half-wits.

They look at their leader and their mouths drool, their eyes roll in oil like a solicitous wife, their fingers twitch; they *love* this little man—he is Thor and Wagner's music and mad thinkers and everything that the German folk have been perverted into for hundreds of years. They dance like decapitated chickens at his glance. They are not really civilized—only badly, on the surface—but under it they are the lousy hordes that fought Caesar in the wilds of Gaul; the *lumpen proletariat,* brawlers of the *Horst Wessel Lied.*

And this jerking little comic is what they want, for he has given them heavy clubs again; this schizophrenic, this dementia lug has given them slogans of blood and power, and soon he will give them death and glory, *gleichschaltung* in

a mass grave. It is hard to believe that there is such a race.
Maybe that is why no one stops him. Maybe that is why the
upper classes in Germany, France and England patted him
on the back and helped him to power. It was Der Führer
under their eyes who turned plebiscites into suicide notes.

IV

The *Herr Reichskanzler* is very happy now as the planes
make one black gout of engines and wings over his head.

He does a little dance step of joy. He turns to a fat man at
his side and shouts into the fat man's ear. He shouts for a
long time, his hand giving him the kiss of an accomplice.

The fat man, a smile all butter, nods. Der Leader smiles
and nods back, puts his fists to his slack mouth, and belches
into his hand with gusto. Then he reclasps his hands over his
little pot belly, leans back, on his boot heels and looks up
into the sun—directly—like a god defying mythology.

He blinks tears, and a black-dressed trooper hands him
a hanky. He wipes his eyes and begins to shout something.
Men hurry away and bring back a little black box and they
open it and take out *Reichswehr* shoulder straps. Men in
uniform, *Standartenführers*—officers, step forward and get
a hard handshake and a new set of shoulder straps. He is
making new generals on the spur of the moment, like a
happy *Pate*—godfather—setting up beers.

He is belching a great deal now. He walks among his
harem of staff officers, his *Leibstandarten,* bodyguard—legs
apart, limbs twitching and with one hand he picks dandruff
from his brown, disordered head, picks absent-mindedly,
then he grabs his pants and belt in both fists, pulls them up
over his fat melon, steps forward, his misformed jaw set
very hard, and shoots out his arm stiff before himself, one
hand still in the belt of his pants. . . .

V

Macht und Erde! power and earth, shout the officers. He
does not move. Stiffly he stands as long lines of shock troops
parade past, their goosestep shaking the very roots of the
earth. Older, blinking reserves, smelling of horse brine,
stamp by.

The staff makes faces behind Der Führer's back and also
put up their arms. They don't like this, but what the hell,
it's a living—and so they stand, he not moving a fraction of
an inch. His face grows red, redder, then almost purple.

The stink of leather, sweat, oil, earth and hot steel is very
strong. Suddenly he tosses his arm down and turns to bark
something in that bad German of his (almost too low
Austrian for some of his dainty staff). A huge, eight-wheel
Mercedes-Benz appears. He tucks himself beside the driver.
Guards and the *beglistenter* men pile in after him, the smoke

of oil grows blue around them, and in a halo of burned gasoline he goes rattling away, like a demented Greek god in a strange chariot; he goes across the Erector toy bridge toward a paper village which his dive bombers have set on fire . . .

And I think of Victor Hugo's remark about Napoleon and I wonder when God will get bored with this one. . . .

THE GUNS

Great guns made by the *Vereinigte Stahlwerke* A.6, bigger than I have ever dreamed of, have been brought up in sections, set into place and now pointing up at the moon (and toward Poland) are firing salvos. Every time they do, Shad Roe closes his eyes and reaches for the flask of raw army rum placed at our disposal. They line the fields, these guns, and sweating happy gunners with muscles of wire rope, keep them snarling. There are thousands of them. 37 mm. anti-aircraft guns, 155 mm. coastal guns, 105 mm. howitzers.

II

The heat is high and it is noon and the men keep marching, but for us favored few there is a long table set under apple trees and very wide, pretty farm girls, their flaxen braids flogging their heavy bodies, walk around us putting down great wooden saucers of spiced meat, thick bread, a cucumber salad and foaming schooners of dark good beer. The *Offizierstager*—the officers' camp—lacks nothing.

We sit with Jap dwarfs hissing into their yellow paws, and grinning Italians, and those favored enough to be invited to witness the thunderbolts of this airedale Thor and eat his *salmis de faisans.*

THE HAPPIEST MAN

The Gestapo has sent the Keg to take care of us and he loves us and sees that we get the best of everything. The Keg is a delight. He is built like a sweating brick wall and wears the Oak Leaves on the Knight's Iron Cross. He is very tall, very wide, but solid—not fat. He enjoys everything in life. He eats with pleasure, he drinks with joy, he pounds

backs and tells us how happy he is, and makes the sign of the Cross with a goose leg.

We have heard stories about him. He is no *verdammte* sourpuss like Himmler and his hangmen. They say the Keg murders people for pure joy. There isn't a mean or sour bone or bit of unhappy gristle in him. His face is scarred by old street fights, his nose is flat against his happy face.

"Life, life," he said, "is good. Not sour like Himmler *der Henchler,* Heydrich *der Henker . . ."*

We drink beer and nod.

He knows two English words: *"Cheesist, by Cheesist*— this is some show, *nein?"*

"Good show," says Shad Roe in his *hochdeutsch.*

"Much more to come. You shall see everything. We are the goddamnedest race you ever saw—no loafing—*nicht hier."*

The Keg laughed, ran his fist up the leg of a passing girl, until she giggled in high glee. Then he went back to eating spiced beef, his big good teeth never bothering to chew until his mouth was full, and then he would gnaw his way free from the shoulder or rump of beef he had in his hands and would chew, the whole large head chewing, until runnels of sweat ran down his great wide neck. Chewing, smiling, telling dreadful low stories about the Leader (he had no respect for anything, even table manners), the Germans, his own Gestapo, the army *dummkopfs.* He would tell us the most fearful outrages, the most dreadful things in the amazing saga of himself, Hitler, Goering, Goebbels and the army *pigdogs,* as he called them.

"You should have seen our leader fall down and wet his pants during the *verdammte* Beer Hall *Putsch* in Munich— ha ha. *Cheesist,* he fell down so hard he threw out his shoulder from place."

We looked around us and went on eating with an attitude of cold, polite attention.

The Keg feared nothing, no one. Wine, food and fat living had colored him like a meerschaum pipe.

"That Goering and Goebbels—millions they have put away in American and English Insurance Companies; well hidden—don't worry—the Insurance Companies prefer business before country . . . *ha ha.* Try some of this pig's pelvis!"

II

He was roaring drunk, his cheeks twitching, his heavy hands were on everyone, his barking laughter grew louder and the hot sun wetted his cropped head until every scar on him burned like a flame. His uniform was wet—great dark spots were wetly staining his armpits, crotch, but, happy in himself, he waved a rib bone at us, a picture of terrible joy, way out of drawing.

"You have seen something today that will rule the world."

"I doubt it," said Shad Roe.

"Ha ha . . . *Cheesist, by Cheesist,* he doubts it! This *verdammte Zeitungen* towel boy doubts it!"

"I do."

"*Cheesist* . . . we will take the world and then, you know, I don't think we will want it."

"Why not?" I asked.

He laughed. "Ha ha, they, the other Nazis—they don't know the world like I do. Murder is only a pleasure, a way to a purpose when the people you murder are fighting you. The hunt, 'the sporting stalk,' as you Englanders say—that's the fun. But once we rule the world, *by Cheesist,* the scum will only die like ants under your boot heel, your *gnadenstoss.* I like them to spit, to struggle, to feel them squirm. That is something, part of a path to a goal. Have some more beer."

"Sure."

III

The Keg I remembered, hunted often with Goering. He told us about it. He and Goering, two large men, drunk and warm in hunting wool and leather—the serfs driving the tame imported game toward them, and then "that goddamn pigdog Goering—*Cheesist by Cheesist*—" how he mowed them down, broke the backs of deer, blew up hares and rabbits into a bloody raw spray of fur and tissue, knocked down elk, big bastards, ja—*they were*—elks high as a house, dying, dunging in agony at their feet, and Herman, the little pig, opening their throats with his silver dagger and standing there shivering, shaking, in pleasure— his red face wet with perverted joy, his loins on fire, his bloody hands shaking at the sight of gasping death. The pleasure of torn fur—fur is a sadist's delight, too— Goering standing there lost, drugged at the killing, until you had to clap Herman on the shoulder and bring him out of it and he looked at you like a lover fresh from a woman, not hearing for a minute what you said, then wiping his face, groaning, tired, sitting down until the next kill. In Herman there is a lot of dirty *quatsch*.

The Keg told it well. "Ja, that Herman—a good man to hunt with but fancy in his pleasures if you know what I mean. Likes little nasty trimming. The way he enjoys the death struggle of animals. *Ha ha*. Me, I just kill them, skin them, eat them and digest them. There is no trickery in me. I am a man from *here* to *here*."

IV

The food was all gone, the table was empty, the wooden saucers were wrecks. We stood up. The Keg stood up, spread his legs very wide apart, patted his stomach, relieved pressure, rubbed his jowls and shouting laughter, howled at some orderlies chattering with the blonde mares.

"On your toes, you *gasthaus* scum. The car for the gentlemen."

"What now?" asked Shad Roe.

The Keg was biting the head off a huge cigar, and while a flame was held to it, he inhaled and his eyelids dropped.

Then the tobacco caught fire and he took clots of smoke into his body and expelled it and looked at the end of the bundle of green-brown leaves with pantomime hilarity.

"Now, you are to see Germans, like angels, floating down from Heaven. You shall see how Germans get out of Heaven, away from a Jewish God and Jewish angels, and come floating down out of the sky with machine guns and sharp knives. Part of the *Fuehrer Prinzip*."

"With parachutes?" I asked.

The Keg said: "With parachutes . . . without, *if* we say so. The Germans—we Germans are stupid enough to obey any order." He thought a moment and looked at me with his innocent happy eyes. "What an idea! . . . I must—yes, I *must* try it . . ."

"What?"

"Without parachutes. *Cheesist*—the *verdammte* fools would do it, too!"

Knowing the race, I was sure they would.

TRAM TALK

"*Amerikaner?*" said the man in brown in the tram.

"Yes."

"Too bad about Philadelphia."

"Why?"

"The Catholics and Jews set it on fire last night."

"Too bad," I said thinking of Chris Morley . . .

Chapter 11

THE FIRES BEGIN TO SPREAD

THE *train through the massed, stippled foliage of the Schwarzwald crept along the silent alleys of trees, and cows with silver bells stood in the clearing chewing sideways their cuds, while truckloads of steel-hatted troops moved over pine paths toward the French border. To take up positions opposite Strasbourg, Colmar, Hagenau and the Great, graft-built Line. Chico, in short leather pants, with a sketch pad and notebook, looked like any other* Wandervögel, *and at night he sat with the innkeeper listening to the suave radio reports of fighting at Gera, Elbrogen and Habersbirk in the Sudetenland . . .*

THERE ARE NO CZECHS, NO POLES

The day Hitler marched into Prague, I was eating a lunch of *ebsen-suppe* with diced *wurstchen*, drinking my two *helles* of Pilsener, and finishing it off with a *käserschmarren* dessert, and the wide fat man in the corner watched me eat and took a pill out of a little blue bottle and swallowed. He had a saturnine obesity, an obscene shaking fatness. He ate more pills and soda water.

"I used to eat well, too," he said. *"Nicht hier."*

"Soon we shall all eat badly," I said. "Join me in a Pilsener."

He came over and sat down and tucked his big belly neatly under the table. "I will have a citronade, thank you. To celebrate Prague."

"After the Czechs—what?" The waiter was at my elbow. *"Bringe noch ein glas Bier und ein Zitronade."*

Pill Eater swallowed another pill from his bottle. He was heavy with lard, his blue eyes suffered in oily skin, his beautiful hands were ringed in suet, his sweet little mouth fought against the puffy cheeks and I could see he had once been a very handsome man. The pill went down. He said: "There are no Czechs. The race never existed."

"No," I said.

"No. I ought to know. I wrote the book proving it."

Pill Eater blinked and looked at a beefy leg with an evasive amiability.

"What are they?"

"Dead men now. We are all dead men. They are deader than any of us at the moment. I am a dead man. I am getting fatter every day. Nothing can stop it. I don't eat. I swallow gland pills, I take treatments. I am humble, yet I grow fatter every day. Dostoevski says, a man who bows down to nothing can never bear the burden of himself."

"And the Poles?" I said.

"There are no Poles, either. I'm working on that book."

"Who publishes you?"

"The state publishing house—Der Führer's, of course, really."

"Do you believe in it at all?"

"The State?"

"Skip that. The books you write."

He ate another pill and shivered as he swallowed his citronade. He looked like a stale Silenus on his last grape.

"Am I a child—am I a fool—am I anything but what I appear? I write what I am told. We must save the German nation—any old scheme to an end. A terrible epidemic—like my strangling fat—of hatred has attacked mankind. I help."

"You think so?"

"Who am I to think? A school teacher from a *Karlstadt Volksschule* with two books on popular scientific subjects behind me. Der Führer—he thinks for me in public."

"For the best? You, a reader of Russian novelists. Remember Herzen's remark on life?"

"I am a student—a teacher. The man of action isn't in me. I must work for the German nation, that is all I know—that, and that the fat is killing me—and that there are no Czechs and Poles."

"And Herzen?" I asked.

He smiled and leaned back and his chins shook. He said:
" 'Life has taught me to think, but thinking has not taught
me to live.' "

"Right," I said. "Do you think there is a Poland?"

"Of course. Once we reach an agreement with the U.S.S.R.,
we march. . . ."

"You think the Russians are fools?" I asked.

"No. They are realists but—you see—I can tell you—I got
this from a friend in Berlin. The English have been at the
Führer to attack Russia and leave the Western front alone.
But his price is too high. The Moscow people know of it.
Hitler sends actual gramophone recordings of everything
Henderson says to them. The Russians now know England
wants to double-cross them and get us and them to fight it
out while the English wait outside of the arena. Well, it will
not be so. A Soviet-Nazi pact, the only protection the Russians have."

"I'd like to bet against that," I said.

"But—of course. *What* shall we wager?"

"A roast goose."

"Please. You know I can't eat. A de luxe edition of *The
Brothers Karamazov*."

"And a case of seltzer water for your health and beauty."
He shivered and looked at me.

" 'Beauty is not only terrible, it is a mysterious thing.
There God and the devil strive for mastery, and the battle-
ground is the heart of men,' said Dmitri Karamazov."

II

In August the walkers and hikers and campers come to the
Black Forest and the sick and dying think they are getting
better and the Inns keep their fiddlers playing Wienerwaltzes

and the beer flows like—like Pilsener beer—and the tired, healthy hikers sit in the tap room singing, singing, usually Goethe's *Wanderers' Night Song.*

Über allen Gipfeln
Ist Ruh
In allen Wipfeln
Spürest du . . .

III

I was reading a letter from Shad Roe, who was in Berlin and having a dreadful time with the Baroness, who was getting more money-mad every day. And there was also a great deal of nonsense about historians and new wars.

At my table there was a very thin pretty Polish girl who had a bad cough and every once in a while she would look into her handkerchief as if counting the number of days of her life lost since morning. I think she had hallucinations of morphia. Her name was Edna and she wanted to go back to Poland but all passports were held up and she existed numbly, alleviating existence by coughing. My own passport was worthless. The American State Department had not approved of me in Spain and had cancelled it. So I sat, too, and waited and the host came over to our table and said:

"*Bitte schön,* a little wine, perhaps . . . ? It's from me."

"Celebrating?"

"Why not? The Russian-German Pact has just been signed."

"Oh." The Polish girl coughed loudly with a sullen smoldering persistence the sick have. She looked into her hanky and sat very still.

"Never mind the wine," I said.

"As you say. It's good for the *Magen*."

IV

Pill Taker came over and sat down. He was bigger than ever—the lard had won two great battles with his face and chin and was advancing down his torso, while his legs fought a rear-guard action, but were swelling into painful, swollen defeat. The struggle for existence was almost over.

"You win," I said.

"No one wins. We who are about to dissolve our identities—" he looked at Edna—"we can just talk some philosophical rigmarole and dress ourselves in flabby theosophical slogans."

"You think the whole world is going to die?" I asked.

"Why not?" He ate two pills and swallowed mineral water and pushed his great stomach to one side and leaned over the tablecloth. "It doesn't matter. Doesn't matter who dies first any more. The Germans, the Poles, the Americans, the coolies—it's all over—see—*all* over."

Edna said: "You used to say there were no Poles."
The hikers at the fire lifted steins and voices:

> *Kaum einen Hauch;*
> *Die vögelein schweigen im Wald . . .*

"There are only people," said Pill Taker. " 'Life can only be understood backwards; but it must be lived forwards. . . .' Soren Kierkegaard knew."

Edna looked at him. He smiled at her. He had once had a lovely smile. They looked at each other. I said: "Maybe you're right. Maybe we are all dead, and today is Judgment Day. Only some will die sooner than others."

"You are drunk," said Pill Taker. "Too many Pilseners."

"Maybe," I said, getting up.

I went to the bar to listen to the shouting radio celebrating. Back at the table Pill Taker and Edna were talking. Suddenly she leaned over and slapped his face. He dragged his balloon of fat to its feet, tried to bow, failed, and came over to the bar. I turned away and looked out at a wet landscape—like a boiled vegetable dinner.

V

"She slapped me."

"I saw," I said.

"I said I knew now there were no Germans—*no* Germans either—and she slapped me."

"Why?"

"She said—it would be too easy for me to die forgiven . . . and she wasn't going to forgive me my lies. She said there *were* Germans and there *were* Poles."

"She's right."

"I guess I *did* want to be forgiven. She could have forgiven me."

"She may."

Warte nur, bald
Ruhest du auch . . .

sang the hikers.

I could hear them singing for a long time before I fell asleep that night. And when I got up in the morning the

Turkish student who drank brandy . . . was still sitting over his brandy, brooding. He could brood for days. Over brandy. He said it wasn't the war talk—but that he just liked to brood over life. It was a large subject, I said, and went in for breakfast.

The Germans were happy in hopes of great victory . . . so I went back to the Turkish student. He hadn't moved, except to lift a brandy to his thoughtful mouth . . .

Book Three

THE LITTLE PEOPLE
GO OUT TO DIE

Chapter 12

TO THE TUNE OF WAGNER

At Mannheim the train would go no farther so I went back to the Inn by bus. Poland had been attacked with some new kind of war. "Counterattack with pursuit." It was very funny (except to the Poles, I suppose). "The whole German people are *Amokläufers,* running amok," said my Swiss barber. "They had waited so long for this hope of ruling the world and now it had come they shiver and pitch in to make it true."

"Take a little off the top," I said.

Troop trains went past, great army cars, huge guns, thousands and thousands of horses—bound for the Palatinate and Rhenish Prussia, and to face the French in their Great Line and perhaps hope the English would not fail the Nazis again, and back down on their Polish promises. Hitler had a coaxing maudlin manner for English lords—and they loved it.

Every German said the English could be counted on to avoid fighting. Der Führer was a smart man, said the Swiss barber, he would take the Poles like he took the Austrians, and the Czechs—then the Balkans—then, in one big bite the French and the English and after that—well, "Lindbergh was a pretty good example of the Americans who wanted no part of fighting the new wonderful Germany," said the barber getting a hot towel. "Yes, it looked as if this is the moment of glory for them."

II

I read the newspapers and tried to get out of Germany. I was no lover of *Der Totale Krieg*—and the *Eintopf* Sunday. Someone had bombed Alexanderplatz and *Vom Winde Verweht* by Margaret Mitchell was still the best seller everywhere. Major Eliot said:

It is my opinion that the Army of Poland is going to give a first-rate account of itself in the struggle which has been thrust upon it . . . The Polish Army will not be easily destroyed nor quickly overwhelmed. . . . The Germans will not have an easy time of it moving large numbers of troops very far inside the Polish frontiers.

III

The *Oberkommandos* are raping and burning Poland. The Keg had died in action before Brest-Litovsk and there are rumors that he was shot in the head from behind (like another Nazi General in disgrace before Warsaw).

Brest-Litovsk has fallen, and I sit in the Inn's tap room listening to the radio boil. I am happy to hear that the British have sunk the *Athenia* with a U-boat bearing Nazi colors. Goebbels is very sure it wasn't a German U-boat as Germans love little children and the newsreels are full of butchered boys and girls and women shot down in Polish fields. Goebbels says some of his best friends are children. I went to see shock troops train down the road.

IV

"The Russians have had to come into Poland to prevent Hitler from rubbing against their border guards," the Swiss barber said this morning. "It is very interesting to see power politics played." The Germans and Russians are very polite to each other but there is no trust among them. "The Russians don't want the Panzers just yet resting their excited heads against the cool Ukraine," said the barber, stropping his razor.

And the French and English announce great victories

against the German Siegfried Wall with dozens of German towns taken. "It's all lies," says the Swiss barber. "Even I know that. There is no action in the West yet."

Hitler says, full victory in 1940, *selbstverständlich*—of course, and then runs out of the Burgerbräu Keller in Munich with all his head men just before the bomb blows up a hundred almost innocent by-sitters. "No one believes this version very much," says the barber who knows everything. "So there is a German lie to balance the French and English ones."

I am going to Berlin to see the Baroness. She can fix this matter of passports. Personal cupidity still has its place in Germany.

The *Graf Spee* has scuttled itself and that, too, is celebrated as a victory. "War *does* affect people's brains," says the Swiss barber. His voice is beginning to jar. . . .

HORSE LOVER

He was a lame tall man with one eye, who had been through the last war and he bred horses, and sometimes brought a few to the Inn for the guests to ride. He was standing in the courtyard, his warped leg ready to fold up under him and his dead eye closed very tight.

"No riders today, Hans?"

"No horses today."

"Off to war?"

"Every damn colt."

"Too bad . . . you had fine horses."

"Horses are very fine people. I don't find many people that are as good, as noble as a horse."

I wanted to ask about Hitler but didn't. "What now?"

"Goats, cows, pigs . . . but my heart isn't in it. . . ."

"Maybe you'll get your horses back?"

"*Nein.* Last war my father had three hundred good fine horses, and twenty stallions at stud . . . They go . . . they die in the stinking mud . . . I saw them in France . . . No, the horses never come back. Horses are smart . . . only men are foolish and come back from the war. Look at me . . . parts of a man. I should have been shot like a hurt horse . . . but no . . . they sent me back in a basket."

"There will be other horses."

He looked at me, scowled, and went away sideways like a lame crab. Everybody said he was a little hurt in the head from a bad kick. . . .

Chapter 13

THE COFFIN COMPANION

THERE are all kind of Germans.

He was a little man—always happy to be intimidated by rich guests—not more than five feet six and he was no longer very young. His job was to collect the muddy boots we left outside our doors and scrape and polish them and he also once rubbed down the now missing riding horses and dug in the kitchen garden and he went to town for the mail on a rusting bike. There was nothing he couldn't do; kind, odorous, redolent of shoe-blacking, manure, tobacco.

He had a huge rubber cup on the end of a wooden club and he struggled with the "Amerikaner" plumbing from morning to night. He pushed the big barrels of beer into a dark cellar and he bathed the dogs. He was always busy, and sometimes a secret elation set him humming and singing low: *"Dreimal hoch."*

His name was Karl and we all called him Little Karl and we called him often. He never said much—just touched his hay-colored hair with two fingers and said *Bitte* and thank you, and went his way smoking a fragment of black pipe. And every morning my shoes were at the door and sometimes I would leave two marks for him. But mostly the healthy guests forgot him and went on working on an anthology of alcoholic drinks.

II

And one morning my shoes were late and I stood at the door waiting for Little Karl. When he appeared with my shoes shining like black mirrors under his arm, he was in army uniform, looking smaller and more out of place than ever in the rough tunic, the baggy pants, the heavy, iron-shod leather boots—still the little, untainted, amiable man.

"I am late," he said.

"You are going away?"

"As you see—to war."

"Aren't you a little old for it? How do you feel?"

"I am what they need. An old front soldier. I feel *echt.*"

"So you feel *echt.*"

I looked at the little man and saw some faded torn war ribbons on his jacket, and of course, a rusting Iron Cross (the Iron Cross is a joke, really. Almost everyone wears one —they are cheap—and they please soldiers—for they make soldiers feel *echt*—fine . . .).

"Come in, Karl, and let's have a drink on your going away."

He swallowed his breath in a pleased manner at this delicate intimacy and followed me into my room and we drank small glasses of Polish plum brandy—good *slivovitz*.

"You see," said Little Karl, "we will finish this thing once and for all . . ."

"What thing?"

"This making of Germany great."

"You want a great Germany?"

"But of course. Der Führer says we must be great."

"I didn't know you were a Nazi, Karl . . ."

"*Ein momentchen*—all Germans are Nazis—more or less, you understand. Some are hot heads, some are lukewarm, some don't care for anything Der Führer says. But in some degree—*bitte schön*—you'll pardon me—every German is a Nazi."

"You think there will be no great trouble—making Germany great?"

"Der Führer has plans."

"I've read them. They are very bizarre."

"You are an educated man."

"Karl, they mean death to millions of Germans. . . ."

"Oh, no! Der Führer says we will outsmart them all. Nothing can stop us. They are old, decayed, fat, and too rich to fight. Like our guests—not you—but the others."

I looked at Little Karl and was suddenly very tired. Little Karl was a good man, an honest man—yet his small ignorant brain was just as excited as a Prussian general's at the idea of world conquest. I refilled the glasses with *slivovitz* slopping the table wet.

"Karl—you are married?"

"But of course so. I have three sons. They are all fighting in Poland."

"Ah—and you—what do you want from life?"

"I? I—nothing. I have a good job. The guests tip fine. I have a good fat, strong wife, three fine strong sons. The Black Forest is like no place else in the world."

"You have seen other places?"

"But of course. I have been every place—Berlin, Paris, London, New York—even Hollywood—*Ja, kein gescheit*— Hollywood."

I looked at Karl and then at the bottle of plum brandy. We hadn't drunk *that* much. "You have been to a great many places."

"But you do not believe. You must understand—a great many rich people come here and die. The liver, the heart, the lungs, something else goes out of focus and, *poof!*— they die. The body is wanted by rich relatives, maybe people remembered in the will. Well, almost twice a year I take a coffin full of rich remains back to some un-German relatives. . . ."

"Forgive me, Karl, for doubting you. Of course there is some law about it."

"Yes. The rich dead cannot travel alone. I have been every place. I travel very well. I sleep on the coffin on the fast trains. I eat well. I have seen the world. So when I say no spot is like the Black Forest, I know."

"But if you are happy here—why go and conquer the world?"

"Der Führer says . . ."

"Never mind the Führer. Think for yourself."

He smiled and stood up. "You will pardon me but I must check the terrines of *foie gras* in the cellar before I leave. I have twenty-four hours, yet."

"Good-bye, Karl. Good luck."

He clicked his heels but didn't look very military; then went away. I was puzzled, with the faintest queasiness sitting on my head. I suppose Germany was full of Karls, all nice, neat, unimportant people going off to fight a war out of the world of Attila. The desiccated standards of the herd instinct had hurt stronger minds than mine. . . .

III

The Inn was very gloomy. The singing hikers were gone to get into uniform, the rich sick sat around dying or getting

better. Pill Taker and Edna were reading Gogol. The radio blared too often and the world went mad to the popping of wireless static. I packed and went down to get my bill. . . . I looked out of the window at the landscape I would most likely never see again. . . .

IV

Little Karl, his army tunic off, was sewing a black band onto one sleeve. He was weeping softly to himself and biting black thread with his teeth and trying to shove it through the eye of a shaking needle. I took the needle from him and threaded it for him.

"I am so sorry," he said, looking at me quizzically bleak. "I didn't expect the guests down so early."

"What has happened?"

"It's my youngest son—Paul—dead."

"Too bad."

"Before Warsaw. I just got the wire."

"It's dreadful news."

"My wife—she is raving mad. The chambermaids are holding her down. We spent all we had on Paul. He was the best—the brightest of them all. He was going to be a *Herr Doktor*—with an office and real gold letters on the window. He was our bright one."

"It's always hard to lose a son."

He sewed neatly, shaking in sorrow. "You were right. You were right. Maybe the Nazis are not right—*Heuchlers* —hypocrites—they wired they had cremated Paul and buried the ashes in Poland."

"I see."

"I have traveled with too many coffins not to know you can't do *that* and respect mankind. People, things . . . things like bodies of loved ones that mean something. . . ."

"War isn't all ceremony."

"If they had only let me go to get the body. I could have come home with the boy. They know me on all the *wagons-lit* trains, all the express trains. I could have gotten the coffin through. But, no! The swine—they had to cremate him and leave him in Poland. It *isn't* right!"

He was very angry. I said nothing. He knew the appalling correctitude of disposing of bodies.

"We even used to take damned Turks back in caskets— and my Paul—ashes . . . No, the Nazis are all wrong. . . ."

Little Karl wept and sewed on his black band and I went over to the desk to pay my bill. The German race's tumultuous life was becoming a little too much for me.

BATH WATER

The bathmistress came into the room and handed me a towel.

"The water is very hot."

"Thanks, I'll grab the bathroom."

"If you want to tip me, do it now . . . I'm going away."

"Is that so?"

"To Poland to run a good clean house for the soldiers."

"That's a strange trade."

"I had a nice place in Brussels in 1918. Were you there?"

"I was just a child then . . ."

"Real cut-glass lamps and red rugs . . . and *very* fine girls . . ."

"I'm sure of it," I said, giving her five marks. . . .

Chapter 14

BERLIN BEFORE BOMBING

Sᴄʜᴜʙᴇʀᴛ's Serenade was popular as ever:

> *Leise fliehen meine Lieder*
> *Durch die Nacht zu dir*
> *In den stillen Hain hernieder*
> *Liebchen, komm zu mir.*

The Germans felt very good and showed it. They are a strange race and the slaughter of the Poles didn't worry them. Berlin was gay with flags and tribal feasting and the broken cross hung everywhere.

There was a huge banner over the building where the Baroness lived and I rang her bell and waited and wondered if they had shot her. They had chopped off a few heads, axed a Polish countess free from her lovely body, and all over the city blood-red posters announced that the sharp blade was murdering Germans in enclosed courtyards.

Goebbels invented a pleasant thing in strict adherence to his warped ape's body and mind—the victims to be tied face up so they could see the heavy weighted blade rushing down toward their twitching necks. A wonderful, jocular race!

II

The Baroness herself answered her doorbell. She looked a little tired and was dressed in a short dressing gown trimmed with some fuzzy colored feathers.

"Ah, my rich American."

"Hello . . ."

"Come in."

The flat was in disorder. Votive candles burned before a St. Antonio. Cold cigars lived in dirty ash trays, someone

had bitten into several chocolates and decided they didn't like the fillings and had left them on a polished table. The Baroness sat down, crossed those famous legs of hers—at the moment stockingless—and she smiled. Behind her a woolly pup hunted something under a cinquecento Florentine mantelpiece.

"It's a fine war."

"Is it?" I asked.

"I shall get very rich from it. Where is Shad Roe?"

"Finland, I think."

"What a dull job he has, the dear man! I am building *Luftschutzkellers*—raid shelters. Business is good."

I inched to the edge of my chair. "I'm having passport trouble."

"And, *ach* . . . you want my help. I warn you—my shelters take up a lot of my time."

"If I can afford it, I want your help."

She patted my face and pinched me. "Always you *Amerikaner*—you *must* bargain. In *Mittel Europa,* people do not bargain—not with me."

"I have no money . . . but some is due me."

"Tell me all about it." She yawned and stretched like a big blonde cat and I told her and she listened and she said it could be done for a price and it ended with me taking her to lunch to eat *echt Russisch* caviar and I felt very proud to be seen with her, although it was like escorting a circus wagon down Main Street. Everyone knew her and had a witty remark or a favor to ask.

III

We went back to her flat and a tall thin officer in iron hat and Iron Cross, with an iron jaw, was there in the hall and he had one perfect rose in one gloved hand and the Baroness was happy to see him. He had oblong feline pupils and an extraordinary spreading nose.

"He is my life insurance," said the Baroness.

We shook hands and it seemed the officer, a *Standartenführer* with a rose, worked in the War Office and did errands for his superiors and for the Baroness and he was a poet or had once been, and he loved roses.

"You, too, a writer? But that is fine," he said.

"I'm not writing much," I said.

"Ah, I'm creating an epic, better than Wagner, bigger than *Faust*— Not based on it—*sie irren Sich*—something—*how* do you say in your country?"

"Terrific?"

"*Schön, schön* . . . terrific."

The Baroness showed us an inch of pink tongue. "Shop talk, you writers. There is a war on."

"My epic is about a god born of sun and lightning and sent to earth to lead a blond race of sun people and fire holders to control of a planet. I have five cantos done."

The Baroness laughed. "Suppose the paper hanger is defeated?"

"Ah, well, I'll just change the opening canto. I started this epic, you understand, years ago. Then Lenin was the central figure; eight years ago some rich, upper-class Englishmen came to me and spoke of T. S. Lawrence, that clown looking for glory—and I was shaping it to fit him. But he killed himself on some gasoline wheels and his friends gave up hope of having him put things in order for them."

"It sounds durable—your epic," I said.

"Of course. The subject doesn't matter. It's the poet that counts."

"That's good."

"You seem unhappy . . ."

"Wars annoy me." I was thinking of Spike. He, too, thought it was the poet who counts.

"But this war is over. Der Führer told us himself that the English lords—the right ones--have promised him a peace now that Poland is ours."

"And the French? Have their 'right ones' approved?"

The Baroness and the Poet laughed; the rose trembled in the gloved hand. "The French, they sit on their stupid Great Line and wait for us to let them live. Most of their leaders have come over to us."

"You are either all mad, or the world is. France may be full of dreadful rich men and foul senile generals hating the Republic, but they hate Germans much more."

The Baroness looked at me. "Let us forget all this and go and have fun. The richer I get, the more I enjoy fun. Hurray for the *Deutsches Nachrichten Buro* and all rumors."

"About France. . . ." I began.

IV

But they didn't want to talk about it any more and we went out and found another girl and we went to several places and had fun as amusing as the Cheyne-Stokes respiration. I tried to have fun. The truth is, I still had hope for France. I knew it was rotten to the core; the bank-church-army groups were destroying it brick by brick, but I felt that against the Nazi hordes they would place themselves in order—every stone, every brick into a united nation holding off a common foe. (But bricks can't do that by themselves.

You see, I wasn't like the "experts" who, later, after the betrayal, came out and said they knew it all the time.)

V

The next morning I settled down to wait for my passport troubles to pass. The French and English wrote of the Great Bore War and the German *panzers* moved up to the Dutch border. . . .

ANNA'S HUSBAND AND THE RABBITS

I had a room near the theatre showing the horror film, *Feuertaufe*. Anna sometimes came to stir the dust in my room and examine the towels and change the soap dish around, thus breaking up the home life of red ants. It was not a very good rooming house and her duties didn't call for her to do more than that in the way of surface cleaning.

She had once been very pretty in a blowzy blonde sort of way, and she looked as if she had been through the mill of minor German novelists and their salacious public; the sort of servant girl who was seduced by slim dainty officers with a pane of glass in one eye, and who, once they had her with child, kicked her from pillow to post. She usually ended up by drowning herself or going to prison for murdering a new-born child. But maybe Anna hadn't done any of those criminal things or literary suffering. And she came in every day at ten, smelling of potato-gin and her blonde hair in disorder and her great breasts bobbing while she stirred the dust off the rug and inspected the roaches eating the paste binding of my books. My world lacked spaciousness and scale for her. A protective strength of gin kept her happy.

Her pink flesh had begun to blotch and her skin was bad. Like all Germans at that time, she smelled bad. All Germany smelled bad. There was almost no soap, hot water was rare and even the best of people were beginning to give off odors—not only of moth balls. One couldn't ride in trams or sit in a theatre listening to Ibsen or Shaw or Mozart without getting a retching nose-full of art and drama and music lovers. The whole race was beginning to reek in its underwear (when it could still have underwear). The lower classes, those poor little people who had been hungry

and dirty and little since 1914, they had always honestly stank. But now even the university professors and the music students were cause to hold one's nose. The race was definitely heavy with nasal horror.

II

Anna had that popular gamey odor mixed with face powder, and potato-gin and old shoe leather. She came in very happy, humming a forbidden tune by an American non-Aryan. She sneezed in the dust she stirred up from the sofa and faced me and smiled—a satisfied nature licking its lips and rubbing its hips.

"You look very happy," I said.

"And why not? My husband is coming home. Marriage ain't spectacular but it's satisfying."

"That's grand."

"And he's not going back to the Navy—*verdammte* tin herring."

"No?"

"He was a gunner on the *Kronprinz E.* And the English airplanes blew his right fingers off—right to *here.*"

"That's too bad."

"Not so bad. He'll come home and get an allowance for life and we'll get us some land and grow potatoes and distill gin and make a fine living. No peddling *Zeitungen* for us."

"Still fingers are fingers."

Anna looked into her feather duster as if seeing all life and martyrdom there. "It's a good wound. Not like poor *Papa.* He was wounded in 1914, in France, and they healed him up and sent him back like a *hund* after rats. He lost two ribs in 1915, in Russia, and they sewed him up and sent him back. He was at Verdun and they took sixteen bits of shell from his legs and behind and healed him up and sent him back. He went up against you Americans and got bayonet stabs *here* and *here* and they sewed him together until he held water and sent him back, stinking like bad drains. He was at Kiel when the red flag went up and the officers beat him over the head with gun butts, but they put a celluloid cup under his scalp and said you're a whole man, and he fought in the Hamburg streets with the Red Guards—the *henkers* just missed him."

"He must have been a very strong man."

"A lot of good *Papa* was after that. He was full of holes plugged by fragments. A regular tin, steel and copper mine he was. You could punch him any place and you'd hit metal. We used to say he'd analyze about fifty dollars a ton as a working mine. All he could do was sit in the parlor on half his rear, rubbing his scars with vaseline and buckling up the belts that held him up when he walked. I tell you on a damp day he threw off sparks, he was so full of metal rubbing together."

"He was a remarkable man," I said, with a thoughtful mien.

Anna rubbed her red nose and yawned, then buttoned her top dress button. "When he died, he just collapsed with a rattle like beer cans falling, and they buried him like old sardine tins and put a cross on him and marked him as a hero. No thank you for such heroes. My husband—he is lucky he's out of it—and what's a finger or two? I've got two big hands, full of *macht*."

"Maybe you're right . . . maybe you're right."

III

I didn't see Anna for a week after that. A new woman was doing the room and she never did more than open the door, stick in a wet gray nose and say: *"Ach,* you are still here, Herr Roosevelt. I'll be back later." And she would slam the door and be back the next day to repeat her performance.

IV

I was walking one day past the Tiergarten and, feeling in the mood, I walked on and passed long lines of *Hausfrauen* standing on line at horse-meat shops—reliving the turbulent years of '17 and '18 and '19—and passing them, I came to a low, cheap café where men stirred one imitation coffee all day, or sat around weak warm beer lamenting the time when the stuff really foamed and didn't need chem-

icals to make it bead to a head. And sitting at a table was
Anna and a tall wide red man with a bound-up arm. She was
wearing a red hat with a broken feather that combed her
nose and he had a naval cap pushed back over a cropped
head, and they were drinking weak yellow beer the color
(and taste, too, I knew) of horse brine. There was no cant
and delusion about them. They were on a bat.

I went over and Anna was very pleased to have an American to introduce to her husband . . . and I sat down and
ordered the dark beer you still could get there then if you
could afford it, or were a Nazi bigwig or an unpatriotic
foreigner.

"To the hero home from the *Krieg*," I said.

The man laughed. "No hero, thank you. I ain't havin'
none of *that*."

"And what do you plan to do now?"

He wiped his mouth with a meaty paw and sighed. "They
have forbidden the making of gin from potatoes. The *erde*
must work for war."

Anna turned a wet, red eye in my direction. "Our hopes
are not shattered. We are going to open a rabbit-meat shop
in the Alexanderplatz. My husband is teaching me skinning."

"Can you get enough rabbits?"

The man laughed. "You don't know wars. My grandfather made half a million marks in the last war skinning
cats to look like bunnies. I know his secret. It's all in the
skinning to make a good rabbit from a sour cat."

I wished them luck . . .

SOME DEAD HAVE GRAVES

They still bury some dead, they still put up banners and
present arms for some recently killed. This is my last day

in Germany and they have brought back the body of the Keg (for, whatever he was and whatever they did to him, to the people in the streets he was a vast and happy hero— a legend of laughing evil—a figure of much pleasure).

II

Chopin's death-music is Polish and they did not use it. They played Schubert's music to Goethe's *Erlkönig* and his *Die Götter Griechenlands*. The square in front of the church was packed and for some reason they did not mind the Lord's Prayer being said over the heavy casket by a thin tall man with a voice like wet fire and a nose like a wedge.

"Und vergieb uns unsere Schulden, wie wir unsern Schuldigen vergeben . . ."

The Gestapo men giggled among themselves and the people in their broken shoe-leather stood rubbing their red cold noses, and suddenly the Lord's Prayer sounded very weak.

"Und führe uns nicht in Versuchung, sondern erlöse uns von dem Übel. Denn Dein ist das Reich und die Kraft und die Herrlichkeit in Ewigkeit, Amen."

"Amen," said a few people and looked in haste at the Gestapo and went away and the casket was commanded in tense commands to move and it walked quickly away on the shoulders of young men (who are all dead in Russia now) and the street was suddenly very still. Hitler had sent a lovely grouping of flowers to an old comrade.

III

The next day there was an order that the Lord's Prayer was not to be used for military funerals of Nazi Party Members.

IV

I haven't been back to Germany since. I remember later
the burial of an English sailor from the iron deck of a
trawler and another man of God reciting over the body. In
German or English or in mangy Latin they do the thing
well. It impresses everyone, I suppose (except the body).

I am the Resurrection and the Life; he that believeth in Me,
though he is dead, yet shall he live: and whosoever liveth and
believeth in Me shall never die. . . .

LANDLADY

The landlady was waiting for me in the little room I had
taken.

"Goodday . . . I hope you are not angry."

"What can I do for you?"

"My little boy heard you are from America."

"And?"

"He would beg of you one stick chewing gum. Forgive me."

I dug a pack out of a batch of soiled shirts. "How old is he?"

"Ten . . . he wants to go Hollywood and marry Shirley Temple."

"He has good taste."

"He loves her and she is very rich and her dot would put us in a good business."

"Your son is a romantic . . "

Chapter 15

DEAR BRAVE LITTLE FINLAND

T HE *Baroness never got that passport for him.*

It was this way: Chico had to get away fast and the only boat he could get was a Swedish ship that didn't bother about his passport, which was no good anyway because the State Department had seen to it that any American who believed in democracy in Spain should not have a valid passport. Mr. Welles was very fair about things like that that could keep help from interfering with the neutral rights of the Spanish Loyalists to die of hunger and lack of weapons. ... so Chico was at Uumaja, eating smorg *until he hated it, and then went to Holmon Island to paint and one day someone cabled* What about Helsingfors? *And what kind of a hero was the White Terrorist, Baron Mannerheim? But they never let Chico see anything much of that war. Only Shad Roe got something.*

PARTS OF LETTERS FROM SHAD ROE
TO CHICO (date lines missing)

Of course I never saw any fighting, my boy, and never saw any front, even with my brave British passport, because, after all, the Finnish people were not very happy about the war, and the meetings in the cities were not the sort of thing the jolly Baron wanted reported to the deluded English and American people who were being fed drama, instead of facts, by Robert Sherwood. There is no fused focus image, really —let's not pity Finland yet. . . .

II

Raumo was the nearest any of us got to anything Finnish and the Red bombers used to come up out of Hangö and blast away and we used to sit in cellars playing poker and drinking the vile native brew and sending out the press reports handed to us and cabling them full rate as news. Thistles and bearded barley grow in fields and the woods are full of wolves, they say . . .

III

"What the hell is going on?" I asked the little man in the wire office who gurgled cordiality at me.

He smiled and looked around him and said: "What do you expect? Mannerheim has been building forts across from Kronstadt for the Nazis—and getting lines ready for the assaults the Germans will some day make on Leningrad. The Russians don't like all that—so they are rubbing out the Baron's threats to their supply line north and south."

"You're crazy, my dear fellow," I said. "It's a brutal assault on a brave little country and the brave little Finns."

He said something in Finnish, then added, as if I were a girl still dewy with trust: "Please, sir, were you here in 1917? No? Well, I was. Baron Mannerheim and his officers ran a sweet White Terror and murdered seventy-five thousand Finns in a terror that Hitler would envy."

"Go on!" I said. "The Baron is a fine gentleman. A gaunt noble rock of pure courage and gallantry."

"Get an *Encyclopedia Britannica* and read up on it. It's all there about the Mannerheim White Terror. You can't call the *Britannica* a red?"

Well, of course, the man was foolish, an impetuous materialist, I thought. Later I found a *Britannica* and it *was* all there! And I suspect someone slipped it in. The reports got more mixed up. Is the whole thing really a Mannerheim war and not a Finnish war?

But if so, the Finns couldn't do much about it because Mannerheim and his crew held the whip hand and all that winter they died like dogs in fox holes around Lake Ladoga and after a while even Bjorneborg was full of Finns with no hands or legs, and they used to build huts and pour water on hot stones and steam their red welts of wounds and protect their empty cause, fearing to expose their own hollowness. . . .

IV

They didn't think much of the war. But they wouldn't talk too much. Just look at you and wink and spit on Mannerheim's picture on the wall and go limping out if they still had one leg left. The lucky ones had even stumps.

I couldn't write *why* the Finns were fighting something they had brought on themselves by building forts for the Germans. No newspaper would print it, and the Finnish Ambassador is society's darling in Washington, so—I'm packed up. . . .

V

It is a dismal land, Chico, that didn't have any fair reason for fighting back, because they had brought it on themselves, and I know the Nazis will get over the phony honeymoon that we English have forced the Russians into, and that the poor stupid Finns will be fighting as slaves of the *Panzer Kings* and everybody will know it—*except* your Washington.

I am nervously dissipating a season in poor hotels in Sweden. It's better to be an "expert" than an honest reporter. It pays better . . .

POST MISTRESS

The post mistress who handed me my mail was very shy and very pretty, but after a while we used to talk.

"You get a lot of letters."

"I have many friends."

"Can you trust them?"

"I think so."

"Be careful. Our best friend said we had a bag of flour in our attic. We have been fined. We no longer have friends."

"I shall try and trust mine . . . a little longer."

"Maybe . . . your friends' letters smell well."

I sniffed the odor of shaving soap on Shad Roe's letter and nodded.

THE LAST BRAWL

In 1918 they had signed what looked like a peace (and smelled like death) and someone gave a party and after that for a long time someone was always giving a party where you could meet women, Gert Stein, art students, men who looked like Sherwood Anderson, small Picassos, smaller James Joyces, and the food was nothing much but the wine was very good because the exchange was just dandy. The

Left Bank, The Right Bank, the Place St. Michel, a suite at
the Ritz, Vive la France, et les pommes de terre frites *and*
the Black Sun Press, and the American Express. And now
France was dying and Chico went to the last party of its kind
in Paris . . .

PARTY PIECE

Stove and the Winch gave that promised party, a literary
evening. A party rich in food, liquor and literary lice, and

wonderful girls and charming people and overstuffed book
lovers and publishers and kind book readers (at least two)
and some fifty other people who came to ignore the guest
of honor and backbite each other with well-made dental
ceramic art. The Nazis were hungry said the wireless.

Stove, he was called that because his people was in the
cast-iron business, was very rich and very kind and very
foolish and he wanted to design stage sets. The Winch wrote
books, of which the second editions were rarer than the first

. . . and she was called the Winch because she was always dragging up some new nine days' wonder to amaze Paris and the arty sets. Mice-swallowers, drugged poets, Kansas fascists on their way to Berlin to broadcast short wave to America, men who bent wire and called it art, gals who wanted to be loved for their minds . . . but the loving was the important part . . . people like that, the Winch was always finding and giving parties for. In the streets the blackout held, the troop trains were crawling toward the Great Line from the Gare de Montparnasse, and Pétain was withdrawing the tanks from the front lines and sending them into the city streets of all French towns, because he hated the little French people more than he did the Nazis and wanted to have no nonsense from them when he sold out his country. . . .

The Winch was in form. She was stripped for action and poured into silver cloth. Her face was clayed and larded and painted with red oils and dusted with blue shadows and marked with planes and tones enough for a Picasso painting. That foppish perfection of a *Vogue* picture sat well on her.

She sniffed the food, drummed her hands against the bar, very slick and smart, and grinned at me.

The large, raftered living room was gay with the trimmings of a party. A huge double door which looked over into the sugar-candy green of the Ile de la Cité framed the landscape between indigo drapes. Many bookcases were full of good tobacco-colored and gilt leather bindings, many small end tables with glass and ceramic objects were pushed against the eggshell-colored walls.

The decorum of the wallpaper was shattered by gay ribbons and the many white cloth-covered buffets that two waiters were trimming, with a last, lingering inspection of a big, smug, roasted turkey with its legs in dainty paper panties.

A whole regiment of red-coated lobsters were lurking with proud crustacean claws in designs of lemons and potato salads. There were also many grills of those deadly Polish paradoxes, spiced pastrami and hard salami. The Swedish mites of fish life were splendid towers of tidbits, and the bar—a whole walnut wall of it—gleaming bravely with polished glassware, marked time for the great pouring to come. Only glamour girls and authors are treated like this.

II

A desperate timidity suddenly gripped me. The Winch checked the wines. Kirschwasser, Cointreau, Golden Wedding, Holland Gin and the many still lifes of absinthe, mint leaves (bruised, *not* crushed), bitters, nutmeg, crème de menthe and Jamaica ginger—an iceberg of cubes and a rose madder bowl of mottled eggs.

A cheerful, bulky bartender was sorting his tools under her eyes. I looked at my watch. Soon.

A Florentine radio was straining out the counterpoint of one of Liszt's *Tzigane Dances,* and the whole gathering of Wedgwood china, Hepplewhite furniture polished to highlights and the copy of a copy of a Flemish tapestry of a Roman rape were neat and cozy under the low-slung lights.

Two Ingres drawings—gifts from a first husband—were on the walls. From a door, there was a glimpse of the bedroom showing the corner of the gilt combination of boat and bed that made the usual claim to being a du Barry item.

Two people were eating *pâté de foie gras* on crackers and trying to keep the crumbs off their bosoms. They were critics. The man was fat and damned *Esquire*-looking in a set of loose, hip-swinging, midnight-blue tails and a high, white-tied winged collar. There was an air of sweet fragility about the woman—very unusual for lady critics.

"It looks fine," said the Lady Critic.

"So fine," added Fat Mouth, his mouth full, "that we have started eating already."

The Winch arranged the great yellow and crimson roses and pursed her lips.

"Now all we need are more guests. Is Hemingway coming?"

"He's off killing things," said the Lady Critic.

"I guess no man can resist Africa. Those damn persuasive travel pictures of breasts and fannies," said Fat Mouth.

The Lady Critic refilled her plate. "I can do without safaris or the charms of big-bottomed Congo sirens. Pass the *lox*."

Then more people came. Some I knew. Some, I didn't want to. Some didn't want to meet me. The bar men sweated, the waiters rolled by with trays and trays. A fat woman and a man with an earphone told me they liked my last book very much but when was I going to write something as good as my first one, *Main Street?*

"There was a book!"

"Yes," I said.

"We liked it."

"Me, too," I said.

"You witty authors."

"Excuse me. Just remembered something. I've got to say hello to a Countess."

III

A little man with the burning eyes and the trim little beard of a minor Italian painting handed the very fat lady in pink a long drink and sipped his sherry, eyeing the crowd around the bar. The fat lady was the Countess. I had known her in Nice. The little man with the beard was de C——. He

knew a lot about paintings and once told me I was a fool
to write. It was kind of him, but I didn't want to earn a
living as a painter slaving for dealers.

We talked of people we all knew and remembered France
in 1928, and watched the party grow wilder. No one any
more came to say hello to me. That's a good sign when
you are the guest of honor.

The Countess ran a small, very pink tongue into her drink.
It was a cat tasting cream. Her eyes looked up at me. "You
look unhappy."

"Just a look."

De C—— twirled his empty glass. The lights caught it
and spun rays over the gathering party. The bar was lined
with black, padded shoulders, with youth, nude and glowing,
with middle age, powdered and fat, with lean figures, with
tailor-warped hips; the radio was louder and people moved
from bedroom to bathroom to sofas, almost always carrying
something to sip or chew on. Voices were shrill and the

great windows were covered with blackout curtains. But there would be no air raids. Laval had arranged it, everyone said. . . .

The drapes fluttered like the wrists of the tall blond boy drinking beer-and-gin.

Very unhappy looks. All artists have them when enjoying themselves.

The tall blond boy shook his wrists at someone. Stove framed the doorway, a great cigar held in his big teeth, his arms full of fancy packages and bottles, a lock of hair in one eye.

"What fun!"

The wireless said the Nazis were dying by the thousands of dampness in the West Wall. A French steel man told me Hitler was dead and that three actors played the part in three shifts. . . .

Only the bones of the turkey were left. They looked like a bird cage. Stove held the great breastbone in his hands and nibbled the tender fat still on it with shiny, audible lips.

I had lost a gal called Grett to someone taller and thinner and was drinking Scotch plain with de C—— and the Countess. She was a great tun, wise and hollow and could splash drinks all night into her soft hulk. The bar man was busy. His eyes were lowered, for he did not approve of his betters acting like swine. He had been raised to respect quality and his illusions were going fast.

The Winch smiled. She had met a great many guests— customer's men, advertising accounts, college friends, debutantes loose on the town, girls who spoke Tenth Avenue and dressed Park, men of title, men of honor, of singular habits, just novelists hunting copy that would become a best seller and take them to the gold mines of Hollywood. She made it her business to meet people. She pointed them out to me.

Long Island polo players and wife-beaters, music com-

posers and conductors, ex-football stars scraping out a living
endorsing things, cold-cream heiresses, oil men, directors of
dirty movies for private showings, air-force men and air-
force women (the latter more male than truck drivers) and
people who held her hand and said, "Delightful party—delightful. Just too, too delightful . . . How did you ever think
up all these clever things? Who's the party for? Huh?"

The man who held her hand the longest was a round,
buttery little buzzard of a man with a cloying voice—half-
lime, half-sugar—who was a critic, a radio mouther, a dis-
coverer of lush talent, a swine in private, a glowing wit in
public, a lecturer in Kansas, a menace to honest writing, a
thing of suet and swill and poison and a power to make and
break any artist who displeased his plush and mid-Victorian
soul, an ardent, eloquent, mean-eyed wonder (his best
friends said he had delusions of gender).

"Oh, Winch—my soul," he said, with his impassive pan
of a face, "at a time when I—poor me—was a newly risen
literary star, I was escorted through a shindig just as this
one by one so dear to my memory now, and told to glow with
wit. Sated but willing, obliging creature that I was, *and*
younger, slimmer too, my shoes I could see in those sainted
days, I rose and spoke a dog poem I had mulled over . . .
and. . . ."

The Thing rolled its eyes, its hawk-nose twisted in the
pink lust of self-pity, its rubber-band mustache shook. . . .

". . . and, as my hostess handed me down from the plat-
form she, in calm kindness, said, 'When *I* introduced Thomas
Wolfe *he* spit at the guests.' "

IV

I escaped from the horrifying vision of literary success.
One of the waiters offered me a wilted watercress sandwich.

He was very sad. His son had died in the phony war outside the Great Wall and his wife's brother had lost an arm in the Great Bore War near Metz and he was going next week . . .

The playwright I had once met in Hollywood sat looking at his hands and then at some drinks. He came to me.

Three full glasses were on the little table. He looked at them and waited for his emotions to drive him to the pickup.

His nerves—shrunken, quaking, repentant—begged. He teased himself along, lifted a glass, watched the color in the light and then, after holding off for a second, downed the drink. The Countess wasted no time on such seething goings-on. She lifted and drank with no monkey business.

"You're a fool," she said to him, "to let the stuff get a grip on you. I take it—but no nonsense, no squalid complication. If it steps out of line, I punish it. I stop drinking."

"That's wonderful," said the Playwright. "But I couldn't. I like to meet my thirst half way—have my inner man snatch at it—feel the stuff boil down within me, settle down to growl and gush, send little, tickling ideas to my mind. No elegance of drinking habits about me. I'm just a lush. I can't stand war. Louie Mayer understands me . . ."

"You're lost if you can't stomp it down, forget it once it's passed your teeth and let it work without bother to you. You're going to be scraped off a wall some day."

"How true! Mud in your eye." He gave us a scythe of a smile.

"Down the hatch."

But I could see that the Countess was drunk, too. The party went on . . . Sirens sounded from St. Germain des Prés . . .

HOW TO HAVE FUN IN A WAR

The Countess opened her mouth and drank, reached for another glass. "Stove promised me something. I'd like to hear those Beatrice Lillie records."

"Of course," I said, going to the gramophone. *"I Hate Spring* is the best one."

The Countess lifted one of her eyebrows. "See if you can dig up *I've Been to a Marvelous Party.* . . . Such inflection! Every intonation perfectly timed!"

The bar man was beginning to wilt, I saw. Such guzzling! *I've be-e-e-n to a mar-r-r-velous party.* . . .

The only two people who had come to meet me were leaving.

"And *Babbitt*—what a book!" she said.

"But all in all," he said, "I guess it's *Arrowsmith* that you worked hardest on."

"No," I said, shaking their hands, "honestly can't say I did any work on it at all."

"Modest," she said. "Not at all what I thought you'd be. I expected an old, hard-bitten man—and you're so young."

I saw them to the door. The party was very loud.

II

More guests came. I knew one of them. The Yale Man. He had written me a kind letter at the time of my first book and had held himself up as a dreadful example of what not to become as a writer. The last of the F. Scott Fitzgerald mob . . .

He greeted me with a flabby hand. "Hi."

"Pretty good," I said. "This way to the bar."

"Swell. See you later. Talk—talk a lot. . . ."

The Yale Man was a writer of small poems and some books that were more whimsy than whamsy (and as usual here—the second editions were much rarer than the first). He earned a living writing market reports, tip sheets and bond sales come-ons for Wall Street brokers, by furnishing chapters to popular novelists stuck for time and ideas and by sponging with detached grace on all his friends. His brain was wonderful, and he ignored it as much as he could.

He had been a Marxist, a Buddhist, a Single Taxer, a Kelley Curer, and once ran for Mayor of the City of New York. His were, no doubt, the best speeches made, but his boys took a terrible beating with blackjacks at the polls from the Tammany hoodlums. He had just entered the Church of England, but was drifting back to Voltaire and a dislike for the Hearst press. He was being seen with phrenologists and Swedenborgians. Really nothing meant very much to him. The only unfortunate thing about him was that he had that first-class brain in a drifting, careless, drink-hungry body. He was a sad mixture of old Unitarian war gods and frivolous poetasters. He had come, he said, to Paris to see it die. . . .

He found the bar. He always did.

The Yale Man and the Art Dealer began trading insults and rum punch.

An Englishman stepped between them.

"Remember me?" said the Englishman. "I bought a *Rinaldo Enchanted* by Tiepolo from you."

"Of course! Sir Charles! Care to sell it back? I can double its price."

"Why?" asked The Yale Man.

"Tiepolo is rare. Two hundred thousand is offered and no picture in sight," I said.

The Yale Man sighed. "No painting in the world is worth more than five hundred dollars, and that goes for the great painters like Blake, Michelangelo, Masaccio, Vermeer, Turner and Breughel. Most of the other sign painters are worth about fifty bucks with their socks and wives thrown in and *some* had fine, fat wives."

"You jest," said Sir Charles with unwonted liveliness.

"Not on your tintype. A good painter can make a nice living on five hundred bucks a canvas. The rest should have their hands chopped off by the state for their pastoral artifices. But it's dealers and buyers like you fellows that cause fancy prices to be paid for junk that should have been burned years ago. Ah, this sumptuous screwing of artists and art! Do you think Botticelli or Van Gogh or Delacroix ever valued a painting as worth over five hundred dollars until you fellows came along and built up a Stock Exchange of Art and said, 'Art is hot stuff. Have some.' The sad part of it all is that no great painter ever made much money from art. Titian did, I know. And Rembrandt did at one time.

But most of the boys died hungry. Enough for them a transitory moment when they touched eternity? Nuts! You're a vampire, eating the stringy hams of dead artists, gnawing on the moldy skulls of long-buried masters. *Ain't* you ashamed of yourself? Your soul is 'old, cold, withered and of intolerable entrails.' "

"Nonsense," said the Art Dealer. "It's all supply and demand. I couldn't sell a retouched photograph if people didn't want it. I'm just dealing in what people want."

"You leave fingerprints on my mind," said the Yale Man.

Sir Charles yawned and winked at me.

"I say, have you any Andrea del Sarto or Rosso Fiorentino, Cosimo Roselli or Sogliani about your place?"

The Yale Man asked, "You really like those wops? Their driveling sensibility?"

Sir Charles smiled. "Not at all. But I have found that early Italians increase in value year after year. I admit they are gloomy, scabby-looking things but really great investments. For pleasure I collect Gillray and Hogarth and fruit pieces by Ghirlandaio."

There was the sound of smashing glassware from the bar and the happy screams of women being touched.

III

"Parties are *sure* fun," said the Yale Man.

"Not when they break things," I said.

Sir Charles and the Art Dealer were busy talking down the price of a Raphael, *Madonna Del Granduca.* I knew it had been painted by a young drug-taking Polish genius in Paris in 1929—a noted and gifted forger of Old Masters— an unsociable devil but a grand paint slinger.

"No breakage, no party," said the Yale Man.

"And a case of Scotch," someone said. "Just in case of snake bite—even if I have to bite the snake myself. Ha, ha!"

I heard voices all around me.

"Fifth edition . . . Fadiman turned green with rage."

"On Fifth Avenue with his garter dragging, and the editor of *Collier's* prancing along to lunch cut him dead."

"He's going—and I didn't want him to. Honest. She had him for four years *once*."

"Hitler is a Jew . . . related to the Rothschilds. . . ."

"Lady Astor promised Von Ribbendroffffff . . ."

"He's like a child on a picnic. So sweet when drunk."

"Ma wants you to have dinner with us tomorrow night, and meet a Hollywood Arab."

"I can't, Mike. Do you think I can, knowing how you feel and—and how I feel? It's no use. I can't get it out of my system unless I write a book about it."

"Here comes that terrible lover of dog stories. Save me from his verbs."

"*If* you come to dinner, wear your Yale pin—our butler is a snob."

"Fine. Oh, Mahatma . . . I want to know—what do you hear from the dress designers?"

Two A.M.

"Wonderful party. Help me find my coat, Maude, honey. I'm an unmitigated, incredible drunken swine."

"Can you walk?"

"That stuff they do on feet? Sure!"

I went into the bedroom to comb my hair. Some music lovers had brought the gramophone in there and were playing Gershwin very low while they lay on the bed and smoked.

Stove was seated on the other bed, drink in hand. A girl was fixing her hair in the dresser mirror with a vacuous, happy expression. A *Paris Herald* reporter said the Nazis were breaking through the forests near Sedan and the woods of Compiègne were burning . . .

II

"Going so early?" said Stove. "Some of the Theatre Guild people are dropping in."

A small girl with big eyes and an open mouth ran into the bedroom. She was followed by a Harvard boy from the American Embassy and both began to strip the beds under people and to pick off shades from the lamps.

I sat down on a chair and grinned. "What is this—a new kind of game?"

The little girl, vaguely perturbed, her mouth full of pillow case, said, "Charades. Jay and I are going to do a honey—pornographic."

Harvard smiled, showing too many teeth. "We're attempt-
ing one of Norman Douglas's limericks. *The* one of St.
Peter and the fairy."

"I hate to miss folklore like *that*. But I'll try and tear
myself away. Good night, Stove."

"Good night. Your party is a success."

"Yes," I said, very humble.

Harvard opened the closet door and took out a bamboo
cane. In the other room the big radio was muffled in talk
now, was losing ground. The little girl came out of the
bathroom holding high a red rubber enema bag. Harvard
was awed by the glorious discovery.

"Oh, boy! *That's* a marvel!"

In the streets the newsboys howled that the Nazis were
murdering Rotterdam, had been forced to march to battle
and would be crushed between the English and French. *La
guerre est finie!*

III

Outside in the doorway it was cold.

The Countess was not what she once had been. She was
very large, and when she was drunk de C—— needed help.
I got a cab and we got her in it and we drove to her apartment house. She was a very old friend. I would have done it
for any old friend. With very great care, de C—— and I
lifted the Countess from the cab and helped her into the
ornate lobby. She was asleep in the elevator and when we
laid her gently down on her bed she was deep in a great
snoring, magnificent, three-masted snoring, all sails spread.
De C—— pulled off her shoes, loosened the garters around
the great thighs and opened her girdle (all the hooks he
could reach without turning over the great bulk). He pulled
the covers over the great chins and then leaned over and
kissed her cheek tenderly.

She was very dear to him. Very. I knew he had been her lover for thirty years—her faithful lover. He knew that their romance was dated, that such things were found only in old books now, books by George Moore and Proust and London's polished Turks. They were tenuous, fragile memories.

The Countess stirred. He tucked in the covers and turned out the lights. Carefully we closed the door behind and went out into the hall. While we waited for the elevator, he lit a long Russian cigarette. An incessant flow of old emotions stirred politely in him, I knew.

"She's never too old for a good time, is she?" he said. "When she is, she will kill herself."

But I am. I hope never to have another party like it. . . .

Four weeks later the Nazis shot de C—— on Laval's orders.

Book Four

EPISODE
FOR KETTLEDRUMS

Chapter 16

A NATION'S LEADERS
STRANGLE IT

Today one may confidently state that the German Army could
not fight the French, single-handed, with any hope of genuine
success. . . . said Major Eliot.

II

In the *June heat everyone knew that something evil was
stirring along the wolf-bitten borders of France and the
panzers were breaking into Holland and Belgium and the
fat queen and the thin king shivered, and the Great Line was
worthless, some said, but everyone still went to parties and
said that Pétain and Laval and Weygand and—"what was
that little stupid general's name? . . ." they would do all
right, back up the "finest army in Europe."*

*Chico, through some error that the War Office was always
making, was allowed to go north to the battles and he kept
a journal and that journal formed the backbone of a certain
section of a novel, called later,* The Sound of an American.
*Here are some of the original parts. Not many changes
were made when they went into the novel.*

HELL, 1940

There was a worthless wornout bag of bones called
Pétain . . .

There was the land French people loved and it was a pretty and fruitful land, and now millions of Frenchmen in tin hats were moving north across the rivers and plains and no one knew how strong, how many, the enemy were and some of us who rode in press cars (when there were still press cars) wondered why the Great Wall had not been built all the way around the nation, and was it true the Nazis had broken through and were riding herd with iron

horses around old battlefields and coming in great gouts of troops over the soil of Northern France? The War Office said only that a great, heroic battle would be fought and won; and the heroes who were to fight it looked at each other and scratched their heroic and lousy beards . . .

II

The faint indentations of fields and the heat of the season seered our eyeballs. It was a June that called for quiet living and shaded windows and cool wine.

III

All day and all night the lorries went north, north, and the men drank army rotgut and got drunk and fought among themselves, and cursed the villages we passed and stopped at stone walls and swallowed the hot stews, and so we went on. Forty kilometers, a hundred, a hundred and fifty kilometers. . . . And tomorrow and tomorrow would see victory.

IV

Rheims, St. Quentin, Guise . . . all saw us pass, dirty men in uniforms, officers, press bums, dusty cars. Grenades dangling from belts, old tin hats knocking together, as they all went to save the Republic. The peasants in the fields did not bother to look at the army, their army, their sons. They piled up their wealth in the form of manure piles and refused to let the men use their wells. The villages scowled and moved us on as quickly as they could toward the *Reichswehr.* The town mayor and the town police guarding their geese herds and cheese houses from soldier-hunger hated the army. They hated the army worse than the enemy, said a soldier, and we went on very tired and hot.

V

That was France, that was the hot dusty June of war with no communiques from the forests of Ardennes . . . that's how it was; many men, not enough machines, no one caring a damn about the army.

VI

All around us the vast army moved forward to help stem the tide. Black men and white men, and Army and Marines, and Spahis from Morocco and Gardes Mobiles. And generals in Rolls Royces and Renaults and *Croix de Guerre* on well-tailored bellies. And on the roads and paths an evacuating population, hesitant and still shy, and knotting up in the regiments, like snarled strings, in the dusty heat.

Always the dust and heat and the goodness of flowing fields and ripe grains and the high scouting Messerschmitts, and so we rolled along the *Route de Grand Circulation*. Mobs of men armed with old broken World War I guns . . . no real tanks . . . no big guns . . . no airplanes of their own overhead. And *singe* meat in cans marked 1922 to eat and gag over and turn bowels to water . . . Maybe some place all the new tools of war were stored. I saw few of them then or later. Yet men—Frenchmen—had grown rich making war tools that never appeared . . .

VII

Then death came sudden and many wings were over us screaming, and half of a regiment was dead in the rut of a ditch and the red blood fell out of tired bodies and so we first met the Stukas, officers howling: *"Planguez-vous!"* And then they were gone to come back again. That's how I always saw the German planes . . .

No one had new guns to stop them. The French just died or ducked and then went on if they were still alive.

Then we walked—spread out—walked slowly bent over (the press car wrecked)—not knowing where we were going and sweating with fear, for death is dreadful, and time and place are things to be feared when the hills look all alike and the woods are dark and no enemy is to be seen . . . and you are only there on a press pass, and what is France to you *or* Hecuba?

VIII

We saw our first French *chars d'assaut*—little light tanks, many of them broken down, their blue-faced crews sitting beside them, smoking cigarettes and wiping oily fingers on dirty pants legs while they spread the plausibility of rumor. Old rusty tanks full of holes and lazy officers and tired crews.

We went on. The cars were for staff officers now. At night we lay in a wood and the stink of death was all around. Horses die sweetly—a strange, sweet odor of ether and sugar and nose-bit comes from a dead horse swelled with gas, dead three days and left in the fields to help posterity's wheat. But men smell bad and we were near the dead. *"Repos,"* said *mon capitaine,* and we all did, among old dead . . . and I felt part of it. But horse stink and man stink made me understand I wasn't a soldier here, and why didn't I join the refugees fleeing south? I didn't.

IX

Day found us on a ridge. Below was a river and a bridge in fragments (like a torn Picasso). Higher up was a bigger bridge and someone had forgotten to blow it up or perhaps didn't want to blow it up. Such things happened all the time and I wondered, but got no answer. The enemy was crossing at the bridge. Thousands of him coming in tanks and trucks and armored cars and that's how I first saw the Nazis at war. Coming fast on our flanks and then our battery of guns went off on our left and it fired and the Stukas came and blinded the guns and they fired a few times eyelessly and then they were silent and we could hear them moving back—those that were still alive and able. We did, too. (It was as simple as that, and that's too simple. People

would ask me for more details later and I didn't have any.
I never got any details. . . .)

It was all a blur of sudden activity, quickly moving back,
then doing it all over again. Men bled. . . .

We fell back to another ridge behind a sick, evacuated
town, the streets full of toy dolls from a gutted shop. A
Compagnie Régimentaire d'Engins came up with their anti-

tank gadgets and we hoped it was all right then but it wasn't,
and the Nazi tanks were coming at us, waddling in a stench
of gas and fire and the too-small anti-tank guns rattled over
them like harmless peas and then suddenly there were no
anti-tank guns and where they were was a hole in the ground
and a flayed, howling captain trying to walk on red stumps,
but of course he couldn't and so he died quickly, stirring
like a broken dog hard hit by a car. I found it singularly in-
triguing, but I was no longer sane and I kept writing notes
and showing my press pass and saying it isn't *my* war . . . !

X

The French were firing at something—nothing ever very real, only tanks, and then they ran; their officers went into a house to look at maps and never came back. It was good to be an officer and I wished I were one. They left us behind as they got into Peugeots and Citroens and Hotchkisses and they drove fast and went away, tired of war. We had to walk. At first they said they were going to look at maps or see what orders *le Grand Quartier Général* had for them, but after that they didn't act ashamed any more and just pulled out of the lines and got into a car and went away, the unsocial devils, and left *"the best army in Europe"* leaderless.

It was something you couldn't believe, but when the men tried to get through on the field phone we found there was no H.Q. No orders. No reserve lines. No nothing. A black savage ferocity went among the men and they knew suddenly it was a sellout in Paris, at board meetings.

XI

There were good men, too, and there were good officers and I joined a regiment just for company. We had an officer —a tall officer—with a big beak of a nose and a habit of winking at us and smiling and telling us we were holding up fine. There were such men—but most weren't. Most ran and left us hot-handed under a cruel immensity of a naked sky, spitting dust, and the hot June days boiling over us.

XII

The captain had us fall back, but in order. The villages were burning now and we took water from any well we wanted and we ate the cheese from the cheese houses and the hens and geese, and ducked under bursting shrapnel and there were more Messerschmitts overhead now and they came low and blasted at us with machine guns and I yelled— *Hey. I'm an American—not at me!* The sullen fast swine. And higher were Junkers 88's that ate up the landscape with bombs and broke the road all around us. We made thirty kilometers the first day, retreating in good order, and I drafted a sharp note to the American Embassy.

Keeping guns and tin hats and stealing drinks; the men were butchering a cow, and we ate it, too, and counted our blisters on our feet and we all hoped that at dawn the lines would hold and the tanks and guns and planes we needed would be there. (You see, it wasn't very real yet—this defeat. . . .) Disaster had not yet hit—it was just as well, our captain said, that the riffraff, the lousy Paris Jockey Club society officers had run off. We would hold out—France had been harder hit before. No one thought of a sellout but I was a little shaky about it all. *I* had seen French generals.

I had been in Spain and lots of places and I knew when an army was holding, and when it was beating back with lines of defense behind it, and I saw no defenses in line or depth behind us. Not one strand of barbed wire.

XIII

Later, people were to ask me, were you scared? were you thrilled? How did it feel to be part of the great battle that may have decided the fate of our fine civilization? And all I could do was shrug my shoulders, because it isn't like that under fire, you don't think of thrills and great battles, you just protect your hide and look for water and puke in ditches and try to keep out of the direct sun, and water old walls and wonder if you will die and what will the big blue flies do to your body. That isn't very heroic or like the story books—but that's the way men in battle are.

And this was a battle even if we saw the enemy very rarely—and he wasn't *my* enemy yet, anyway. Lindbergh didn't want him for an enemy and all I wanted was to get to Paris, and to get to Lisbon, and to get to London, and maybe go home . . . and tell them a few things they wouldn't listen to. . . .

XIV

In the morning under a sky like blue porcelain I was awakened by the crowing of a late lost cock. I lay awhile on the smoking turf, by the stinking burning villages, the shade of a tormented tree keeping some of the sun from my eyes. The salmon-pink road was beginning to fill up with refugees and broken regiments and the higher officers in big fleeing cars.

I could see the sprawled body of a peasant lying in the field, his head a sponge of insects. I could hear the distant talking of the guns, and the clatter of tank gears in mesh.

The Germans were very near and I could close my eyes, and like a blind palmist, feel them like ridges filling the land, creeping, moving in to end France. *Two kilometers away,* said the refugees. *Two kilometers to the rear, to the right, to the left; even,* some said, *to the front.* But that wasn't true. There was panic now—there was that fear, that eye-popping fear that people get, that salty ammonia smell, too, that acid armpit-odor of wet fear. We had it, the refugees had it. Guns began to pass like shrill Offenbach brass music, guns going away, tanks going away (Weygand and Pétain were sending them to French cities to calm down Frenchmen who still wanted to fight. Oh, yes, *this* I saw myself later. . . .)

XV

We walked on, eating stale bread and soaking up bad wine, but the roads were no good. Miles of them stretched ahead and behind us—all kinds of people staggered and fought and fell into the dry ditches. I have never seen such a multitude of people fleeing in such a splashing, fluttering sun, and it was a real mistake to let them fill the roads like that.

The captain said it was the enemy who had started the refugees, who kept them moving to keep the army tossing in disorder. But what army? There was no army under this Wedgwood sky—only a rabble—and I, who wasn't a soldier —part of the rabble. I was no longer important, no one asked to see my pass. I sent no news items to fill out the full life of the comic sections back home.

XVI

They were no longer an army marching on the great bare bones of the French earth. Almost all the officers were gone. They had all the cars and they went off down the packed roads knocking down refugees and banging into wet-nostriled gun horses mad with fear.

Then no mercy sat in the sky, and the Stukas and Messerschmitts were back with many Fokkers, and I would shake like a coward. They would sweep down and spray the little children with machine guns and burn holes into families gathered in lumps around their livestock, and kill kill kill and maim all they could reach. Don't ask me to love Germans.

They had a wonderful trick. They wanted the roads saved for their later progress. They would bomb the sides of fields facing it and throw their shards of death across the roads without harming them. But they harmed a lot of people. But what had happened to the army? There were jonquils and yellow roses along the roads, but where was the army? Why should there be flowers and no army? I was a little sunstruck and my mind was a little battered. I wanted to get away, go away . . . some place the wounded didn't moan so. . . .

XVII

There I was, worried because the French army wasn't holding together and wasn't standing up to fight, wasn't getting big guns and tanks and planes. But of course they weren't sending any. (They were a long way back, the generals—talking, deciding how the selling-out was to be done—how to finish off this Republic that all the old generals hated . . . hated. . . .)

XVIII

The army lay in the ditches, discarded guns and tin hats and canned meat and bayonets and long strands of bloody bandages, and it huddled in little bundles of gory rags, as men died at the feet of old trees and were puffed out into a flaying moisture by bombs. I walked in mustard-gilt hazes of shell showers ducking singing hot iron. I no longer said I was an American and that it wasn't my show.

RETREAT

They were almost in rank once, and at last we hit a huge highway and mounted police were driving the refugees into the woods and they marched then and the men were very mad and many cried. Many could not stop their tears and from yellow teeth and parched mouths and from red faces they kept shouting in despair . . . gesticulating, galvanizing, twitching their dirty faces. Danton, Napoleon, Joffre had seen such faces once.

"Damn Pétain!"

"Damn Laval . . . *La ligne Pétain!*"

"Goddamn Weygand . . . Goddamn Gamelin!"

"Damn Pétain!"

"Damn Laval . . ."

"God damn . . . *à bas les bourgeois!*"

And they damned everyone, anything else they could think of: diplomats, scholars, savants, with monstrous oaths. They knew suddenly what kind of a defeat it was.

II

They were very tired, they were hungry, dropped guns and gas masks and tin hats and packs and scrouged on and kept their bayonets and opened canned stinking beef that had been packed ages ago and was so foul that we ate it, (when we had to) holding our noses, mouthing in distaste the green filth the French meat packers had grown rich on. Our positions grew conspicuously worse. . . . And the worst was getting no news, not knowing how the old generals were doing things. Maybe it's just as well. (Ah, those Frenchmen who cut the throat of France—how we cursed them.)

III

At noon bad Frenchmen shot our long-nosed captain. It was not a good thing to do. It was a mean thing to do. Stupid men stood at the crossroads and they pulled black men, and men with noses they did not like, to one side and they shot them. They had shot a brave man, those bad Frenchmen, when they shot our captain. They felt very good about it. As we passed them we ducked, fearing to say one word for our captain. We just passed, looking back into blood-red faces and drunken eyeballs. We went on, the horrible pollution of those red, fey faces working on our ranks. They would have shot me, only dust was over everyone and we all looked alike below the neck.

"Damn Pétain . . ."

"Damn Laval . . ."

"*La ligne . . . les bourgeois!*"

"Goddamn Weygand and Gamelin . . ."[23]

MEN OF ILL WILL

We passed a great lawn where sheep ate the tailored turf and there was a stone house of age and pomp; it sat back on its rump among many fir trees. Men crossed the lawn to see us. They carried shotguns and hunting bags from which rabbits and pheasants protruded limply . . . cadavers of brushed fur and rumpled feathers . . . The landed squires had been hunting game . . . not Germans.

The unsympathetic fleshy faces of the men looked at us as we passed. These well-fed faces . . . these shaved, tailored gentlemen had been hunting—little animals—while Nazis hunted us.

II

I had seen this French sportsman before. France could die, Europe could boil over. He must hunt and kill little warm animals and bring them to his chef and eat them in grinding mouthfuls with sherry sauce and mushrooms and truffles and a red Burgundy wine, after sucking out the marrow of little bones, sucking them dry, and belching in pleasure at the tender memory of his gorging.

The sportsman liked the kidneys and inner organs nicely done with diced onions and bay leaves and served piping hot. They did not look hungry as we passed. They stood on the fine lawn and they were suddenly very cunning, no longer squandering their patrimony on the army. They did not speak to the men—defeated Frenchmen. They planned of the future . . . after they had eaten their little animals and spit out the tender sucked bones and digested them in the smoke of twenty-franc cigars.

"What tramps."

"And we expected *them* to save France!"

"I wonder if Pétain has reached Hitler with the terms yet?"

"The sooner the better—the neater things will be."

III

So, passing on dirty tired feet, we learned that Pétain and Weygand had given up the fight and were resting on their knees, in humble postures, and the eaters of little animals were making the best of the best of all possible worlds. . . .

IV

Der Führer was at Compiègne . . .

V

I was happy I was not French. I was sad for Frenchmen. I saw these men go down in a defeat they didn't make. But some did fight, and many died and many lost limbs.

I left men I had marched with so long. I cut west and found some English newspapermen reading old copies of the London *Times*. They were not scared, they said to me. Just a jolly muddle—this *blitz* stuff was a business for German savages.

VI

But I was scared, and I went on south and I worked my way toward Paris. The peace terms were not yet forthcoming, the Germans were always just behind, just to the right, to the left . . . three, two kilometers. I never saw them. But once I heard them singing, *Wir marschieren nach Frankreich hinein,* in voices Caesar must have heard in Gaul from blond barbarians.

VII

Sometimes I saw French dead. Always I saw dead horses and everywhere the panic of refugees boiled over the roads making any kind of military progress impossible. I could only advance as part of a mob and hear their bleating cries: *La guerre n'est pas finie* . . . the war is not over . . .

They no longer cursed. They could not talk, only croak. Stomachs rumbled, our breath was thick and coated. They were in despair . . . and then suddenly they knew—betrayed by mean people talking banal humane phrases, by mills and banks and fauns in top hats. France gave a little shiver in the hot sun and died. I saw it. . . .

VIII

We had found a car—a rattling Citroen—nothing much, but we came with it to a great gas dump and saw hundreds of tanks of petrol guarded by police.

"Spare a few litres . . . ?" we asked the first guard.

"Nothing doing. Keep going."

"Hell, man. *Tant pis pour vous.* The Germans will get it all. Three litres."

"Orders—not a drop to be given without the proper papers."

"Are you going to burn it all?"

"Don't know. Move on."

We moved. We were unarmed. We were very weak. We didn't care—or feel horror. And those bridges no one blew up, those food dumps, those gasoline tanks, those mills and factories—the Nazis have them all today. I don't know *who* and I don't know *why.*

IX

We walked. There was no gas for us. We passed great factories very still and packed with more oil cans and finished steel, and with food and blankets and tires. But always the police guarded them and stood by as ordered. Nothing for the soldiers and *move on . . . move on. . . .* Behind, the Nazis came to collect the rich spoils. Did they know it waited?

More mills, factories, gasoline dumps, railroad yards, terminals, powerhouses, bridges—everything was being protected. Cherished for the Germans behind us? Was it full War Office betrayal? Or was it the mill owners and factory-bank-church stockholders protecting their investments, thinking perhaps to keep producing even for the enemy? *Dividends don't take sides . . .* the eaters of little animals say over their hunt breakfasts. I have had many breakfasts with them. I have heard it so.

Paris, Lisbon, London, America. I kept thinking that. I no longer cared either what they did to France. . . .

X

Night fell on the full week of retreat. I could not go on.
My feet hurt, my heart was tired and it flapped inside me,
like a bird, on the bars of my ribs.

I sat by the road, watching men stumble, watching women
fall dead in ditches, watching dirty, sour-smelling babies
make gestures of fear, and howl. It was just a cinema to me.
Not real men or women or babies.

XI

I could see the city of Paris far off. The Military Police
were not allowing any privates, French soldiers, into the
city. The proprietary class was dusting it ready for the new
masters. But I had a pass. I could go to Paris. I had a bank
account. . . .

I stood by the road. Great columns of smoke filled the sky
and some said the Germans were using a new kind of smoke
screen . . . some said they had a gas that could put everyone
to sleep, some said the British had been pushed into the sea
and were swimming home . . . some said in the burning
villages Frenchmen were donning Nazi colors.

There were all kinds of voices.

"They say the Nazis will enter Paris tomorrow."

"Nonsense. Paris can hold out for months."

"Thank God, my gold is in Swiss banks."

"Paris has been declared an open town."

"I have four daughters and no *dots* for them."

"Damn Pétain."

"I shipped my Renoirs to Hollywood."

"I wonder if all the cows were covered on the farm."

"Funny, it wasn't like this in 1914. I was there. The

officers were bastards then, too, but they didn't grab cars
and load up their fat mamas and paintings and run for it."
  "My wife is pregnant in Nice."
  "Look at them junk lovers."

XII

The rank and file stood watching car after car loaded
with silver dishes and old paintings and rare rugs and fine

leather bags moving down the road. They had gas and they
had enough papers to get through to Paris. Most of the
drivers were officers in uniform or their orderlies; bonds,
not battles, worried them. No one cared for the common
soldier any more, and we just stood and waited for the
advance guard of the enemy to herd us behind barbed wire.
It was a sad spectacle—the people in their cars hugging their
treasures.

I got a lift, at last, to Paris in the car of the Countess du ——.

Paris waited . . .

XIII

The streets were empty. The bars were empty. The drunks had gone to sleep off a great defeat. Everyone seemed to have hidden indoors or gone away. The Germans had announced their hour of entry into Paris. The jewelers raised prices and set their watches. Paris waited, a quaint tenderness in the green parks, an astringent perfection of details on her buildings. Dumas, Mainbocher, Henri IV, Chanel, Daumier, *The Afternoon of a Faun*—all waited for the Nazis.

There was still a strong biting tang of smoke in the air. Soot suddenly fell like black snow on the street and far off some siren was sounding as if a short circuit had set it off. The Terror, the Second Empire, Café du Dome, waited. A light warm wind stirred the old copies of *Le Matin, Paris Soir,* old cigarette packages and orange peel in the gutters. The siren died in mid-madness. All was still again. A bit of tinfoil danced in the sun that broke through the new smoke, and underground the Metro had stopped running. I went away quickly. Paris tied naked to the bed was a terrifying reality. I must get to Lisbon. . . .

XIV

I found a cab driven by one of the last of the White Russians. He bargained a long time. We drove by many streets. No attempt had been made to prepare, to really defend the city. Some public buildings were curled in the steel hairs of barbed wire, and some of the alleys had been blocked off and painted with big red crosses. Archaic goddesses girdled in sand bags stood in fashionable store win-

dows, and the interior decorators were not skipping by as
usual for a long lunch hour.

On the way there was music near the Arc de Triomphe.
We turned and saw a long column of machine-cast Germans,
stiffly, robotly, marching. Their officers rode in dusty, heavy
six-wheeled cars, and more stiff, clay-modeled troops followed in eight-tired lorries. Then there was another band

and marching men again in polished coal scuttles, kicking
iron heels into stone streets, keeping time to a marching
step, the sad sun touching the silver of bare steel over their
heads. It was meditative morose vindictive toy-soldier stuff.
It was stale stuff by tribal savages winning the victor's right
to rape.

XV

The Germans went on marching down the Place de la
Concorde. There was a huge swastika on the Hotel de Ville.
It was the last thing I remember in Paris.

THE LAST PLANE

The two little men wearing blue felt hats were sweating and looking down from the plane at the calm fields. One said to me: "You saw it?"

"I saw it."

"How can you say it . . . the great French army is no more."

"It's gone."

The other brother said: "You were there . . . you saw it?"

"Yes. I was, I saw."

The two brothers looked at each other. Then at the other people in the plane.

"He says the Germans are moving south from Paris."

"Pétain, he says, has sold us out."

"But the army?"

"It cost so much."

"My son-in-law is at Metz."

"Everything is untrue."

"He is an American."

"He thinks it's all a cinema film."

"He's right. It's all over. We lost . . . that's all."

"But how?"

"It's no skin off my nose."

"My father died at Verdun."

"Sh . . . my wife is weeping, she's sick."

"What did she eat?" asked one of the brothers.

Chapter 17

THE VENT

Twelve *miles up the Tagus River stands Lisbon, and the chatter and howl, and the very many people trying to get their papers in order and their tired bodies onto ships and planes is something out of the Red Sea crossing of Moses and his people. (Only here Chico found there were more gentiles than Jews, and the Egyptians peddle rugs. . . .)*

The great square, the Traca do Commercio, was packed with people waiting in the white sun, and the very rich gentile refugees with their diamonds sewed in their Russian sable coats, and into their Brussels-lace drawers, and smoking dollar cigars, went to the Aviz Palace where there were no Nazis, and the Germans said bitte schön *and went to the de luxe Palacio Hotel. The Portuguese bowed to earn a few escudos. . . . The rag, tag and bob stood in lines outside the American Export Lines. Even the gossip was twice life-size; and the international spies had union shop rules, said the wits. . . .*

LISBON LULLABY

The days cooked slowly in hot rumor-filled streets.

The hotel porter was an educated man; I used to sit in the lobby and hear him as he turned the revolving doors saying, *Entrez, Herein, Enter, Avanti,* and when I got tired of that I would go into the tea room run by two decaying Englishwomen. They had a rich Edith Wharton atmosphere. They served tea full of dog's hair, while they hugged little smelly dogs to their oily breasts and I thought of Aldous Huxley's words about why disappointed people perverted themselves with stupid little animals:

Many more men and women leave the world for the kennel than for the cloister, and with good cause; in the kennel even the feeblest and dullest of human beings can feel himself the master, the genius, positively the god . . .

Disappointed humans discover among the fleas and the dog-dung, a kind of paradise of wish-fulfillment. They are grateful to their pets—hysterically so at times, almost insanely. . . .

II

Which was all right as far as it went—and it went far enough for me. There was a German, looking like a char-acter gnawed by rats, who always sat across the way from me, who watched me very closely and who, I suspected, was a Gestapo agent sent to do me in. He would eat in slow small bites, chewing hard, and maternally kiss his napkin after every bite. In time I learned he was once a rich German industrialist who had backed Hitler with millions of dollars. And tried to get Henry Ford to back him, too. When Hitler had wrung him dry the German industrialist found he had met his match. So he had grabbed his gold and diamonds and had run to Lisbon and he sat every day across from me. Shivering and eating, and kissing his napkin after every bite, thinking I was a Gestapo agent sent to do him in. So we had our bit of melodrama and shakes and sweats, for after all we were not important enough any more for the Gestapo to waste a wolf on. So we all sat; gnawed rat, a comedienne from the Grand Guignol, pederasts, ballet lovers, a dozen others. . . .

III

In the afternoon, after telling the bus boy you didn't want his ten-year-old sister, you went to your Embassy and were insulted by Harvard frumps and had your papers re-stamped, and the idea that as an American of good standing again, you had some rights, was bounced out of you by the apathetic clerks—most of whom were parlor fascists anyway; empty people, afraid to be kind because it would expose their hollowness.

I pinned my papers together and wondered when I would get a plane to London, and I went down the steps and a long line of people watched me, happy for me: I was an American; and not too much in love with me, because I still had a country to go to. There was a young woman with an uncombed head of hair who sat, a weary arc of disappointment, on a paper valise, her dress open and a rash-marked, sour baby sucked her breast and grunted, and I saw it was

Annabelle—Annabelle, very thin, very tired and very unhappy—wearing tattered espadrilles and no stockings.

I said: "Hello, Annabelle."

She began to weep economically, using only two big tears,
and said: "Chico, Chico, Chico!" and so I led her and the
pigging baby into a private office and I patted her dirty
hand and kissed her hot cheek and the baby smelled bad. I
made up a silly monologue. After a while we got down to
cases.

"You left in a hurry?" I asked.

"Yes. Very much in a hurry."

"You're all right. The British Embassy will fix you up and
get you on a plane. You're English. What are you doing
here?"

"I'm not English any more. I'm the Baroness de ———."

"Well, shut my mouth. Right out of *A La Recherche du
Temps Perdu* . . ."

She pointed to the baby staring at me with eyes out of a
painting of Louis XIII. "This is the next Baron de ———."

"He looks it. But what are you doing here?"

"The British Embassy will not do anything for me."

"And . . . ?"

"The Baron is connected in some wrong, concealed irreg-
ularity with the Lafayette family. The Americans *may* give
me papers."

"What happened to the Baron?"

She didn't answer and seemed to turn her emotions into
goose flesh, and the baby cried and she gave him a pat and
covered her breast and he twisted some buttons on her dress
and fell asleep, disdainful, superior to us who would never
be a Baron out of *La Prisonnière.*

"Was it bad?" I asked.

"It was hell. I've walked for weeks. I've done things to
get rides. I've begged like a lousy beggar for water, for milk

for the kid. It was very bad, Chico, but I made it. When
I get back my thought sequences, I'll tell you—no, I'll *never*
tell."

"Look, weren't you and the Baron good fascists?"

"The best. Didn't we help in the sellout of France with
Weygand, didn't we do everything to ruin France? Yes,
Chico, we did—just like Pétain—Laval—all the swine."

"Then why this—and you here with the baby?"

"Give me a gasper."

I put a cigarette in her mouth and lit it and she sighed.
"Jesus, real American cigs! Chico, I guess I'm not a lousy
fascist. I guess I'm just a freedom-loving bum the way I've
always been."

"But the big love, the great romance of your life?"

She handed me the baby, profoundly pessimistic. "Here,
hold a traitor's son."

"You used to be pretty proud of him when he was only as
big as a grapefruit."

"He's all right. Hell, don't, Chico—don't peddle twinges
of compunction. I've got all the proper feelings for him,
from diapers to the desire to have him set the world on fire.
Only I hate his father now. He did something I couldn't
forgive . . ."

"A noble son of France, of the best families, of the best
factories, of the best people, and of the best churches and
banks . . . ?"

"I was in love, I could string along, fool myself I felt the
way he felt. Fascist, democratic, free people, slave people
—what the devil, chum—it was all words to me. I was
happy; it was amusing. But when my little husband turned
over lists of Frenchmen he wanted shot, turned them over
direct to the Gestapo—lists of Frenchmen—soldiers, workers, labor leaders, political people that he and Laval and
Pétain (who wets his clothing day and night like the tike

here) . . . wanted them murdered by the Germans—I couldn't stand it. I could stand the big factories, the ships, the supplies, handed over to the Nazis; after all, stockholders had to live; I could stand the art treasures and the food being shipped to Berlin—*we* had a good stock of everything hidden. But that last . . . when I found out my own gardener —an old man—had been handed over to be murdered because he voted for the Popular Front . . . well—know what I did?"

"Scrammed."

IV

She smiled for the first time and I gave her another cigarette. And that clear, insolent eye of hers was back. "But first I hit the Baron over the head with a rare clock, and then I grabbed the kid and got in with a group of refugees heading for Spain and kept going. It wasn't anything I care to talk about. It was very degrading, what happened to me—the wrathful, quivering submissions I made, what I did to get here—but I'm taking the kid, and going any place that will have me."

"Hungry?" I asked as a blind soldier tapped past us.

"Sometimes. I don't function normally any more. Know what I mean? Food, shelter, I grab them when I get them— don't miss them unless I'm pretty far gone. The proximity of death, rape, hunger—it's all a daily routine now. I'm shock proof."

"Come on. I know a place for steak—not horse steak, either."

"Chico?"

"Yes?"

"Remember that day in Paris—you and I and Spike, that *ténébreux?*"

"Spike's in Italy—writing epics."

"He'll come out of it, too, like I did."

"Maybe."

"I said I was a fascist and you said you were going to learn to hate me. Well, take your *revanche*."

"I'm sorry. I lose my hates quickly, sometimes."

"Well, hate me and be tough. Otherwise you're going to be licked."

I laughed. "Listen, Annabelle, you can't say that to America yet."

"No?"

"Guess what?"

"What?" she asked.

"The American newspapers are already planning the peace and how kindly they will ask the victors to treat a misled Germany. . . ."

She blazed. "The fools! The bloody fools! Don't they realize the Nazis have plans to enslave them?"

"No, they don't. They think, like the babbling air heroes, that Hitler is going to enjoy the future kindly. . . ."

"They'll learn—all those fake Americans," said Annabelle. "Where is this food you speak of?"

"Near here."

The baby who would one day be a Baron, opened his eyes and grunted and made a smile, a smile squashily overripe.

"Hello, lug," I said.

"*Appohaga,*" said the little mouth with a guileless belch.

Annabelle began to comb her hair. "The voice of the New Order in Europe and the Wave of the Future speaks."

That was one thing you had to admire in Annabelle; she had bounce and could always come back to almost within reach of her last peak. But she would never be as pretty again as she had once been. That ivory transparency, that proud serenity. . . . A coarse humid rankness of swarming humanity, of troubles and fears, had scarred her.

Arm in arm, like opera lovers, we strolled away. . . .

V

When later I got Annabelle and the future fascist ruler of Europe in 1990 (stranger things have happened) onto a boat going to New York, I felt better. It was a strange boat that had been sent over to pick up Americans.

"But as most of the gentile refugees," a travel agency man told me, "had pull with the American snobs in American Embassies in Europe, a lot of good poor American tourists were dragged off the ship, and their places taken by rich gentile refugees who knew that all the answers the world ever needed were sewed up with the diamonds in their mink and sable coats."

"Really," I said.

"Oh, yes. Jesuits, trained reactionaries who had murdered

the little people in Vienna and helped get Austria ready for Hitler; they got on the boat—and a lot of Polish and Dutch and *Mittel Europa* swine—counts and bankers and landowners who had fled in time and had stocked their cash holdings with the Chase Bank—and are going to America now to wait while the little people left behind died recovering their holdings from Hitler . . ."

"There must be a few nice people among refugees," I said.

"The poor, the middle-class—they can't get visas, can't get money to travel. The traitors, frauds, loafers, endowed bums to spoil American colleges, perverts, designers of degeneracies, the noble titles, the sort of scum America could do well without—they are on that ship supposed to be used for Americans."

"Oh, well," I said, "somebody must love a rich refugee."

Well, what could I do? I could get on the ship (maybe) . . . and go home and howl warning, but I was no Ham Fish and no one would listen to me—not as they listen to Jack Benny or Fadiman—listen in time to understand the dreadful things Europe was brewing for the hills and trees and fields and people I loved very much. So I went to London because in London I had a few friends I could talk to and the people were waking up from the great English heartache on the beach at Dunkirk. And so I went to London and played jig-saw puzzle with the ruins of the great air raids, trying to remember how it all was once put together—but the jig-saw puzzle was too big and there were too many parts. . . .

OH, ENGLAND

Listen to the Fifth Column talk in London.
"The English armies are still fighting too many brilliant

rear guard actions; there are still too many old school ties under empty bone pots and not enough great English generals are safely buried in Westminster Abbey." "And Hong Kong and Singapore and Burma and India and Tobruk stand no longer as safe as the solid concrete lions under the nose of Lord Nelson in Trafalgar Square." "The great devastating

air raids come no more to England, and those women and children who still die on English soil are buried like heroes —dead heroes—and a Peer in the House of Lords gets up to defend Hitler and say we must not bomb the German cities in turn . . ." "And the best thing we have to be proud of, is the bloody butchery that pigs get, that we have taken on the shore at Dunkirk . . ."

Chico didn't like such voices.

THE PARTY

There were still a few Fifth Column nests . . .

A brilliant international gathering. Alec Jeek had been there, the hostess told me, "and with a box of chocolates which he said he had brought across the sea for Lady Astor. It was, he said, as good a reason as any for making the trip." And a lot of delightful people in evening clothes—beautiful, fine-smelling girls, and charming medal-hung desk officers from Oxford. You get to enjoy the smell of washed bodies. They were all sitting around a white piano, while an international homosexual with beautiful diction (who had just been nabbed by the Home Office for hiding his assets and cheating on his income tax) led them in a mocking cockney song that no cockney ever sang . . .

> The regiment 'as gone awiy
> And what will all the lidies siy
> When they find themselves in the family wiy
> With 'arf a crown a week for piy!

II

And as the cockneys were all in the East End holding their buggy, dirty bombed heads, and trying to get enough to eat on ration cards, the Episcopal butler passed among us and we pigged in expensive simplicity—I more than the rest—on smoked grouse and goose liver and truffles, and the charming fairy led in another cockney verse . . .

> It's the sime the 'ole world over,
> It's the pore what gits the blime,
> It's the rich 'as all the pleasure.
> Hain't it a bloody shime?

III

I didn't stay for high tea. "With real cream," said the hostess. I went to look for Shad Roe. who was somewhere in England, but whom I was always missing. The people in the streets went about their business, not singing at all. They looked tired but willing; not as tired as the Germans, and not as willing as the upper classes to laugh off the war; and in the churches they were singing.

I stopped to hear Cowper's hymn under a tattered curtain of broken glass that had once been a stained-glass rose window.

> Ye fearful saints, fresh courage take;
> The clouds ye so much dread
> Are big with mercy, and shall break
> In blessings on your head. . . .

IV

It was very still when they finished singing and I could hear the traffic moving around the roped-off block where they were still repairing the gas and water mains from the great mass bombing raids that had as yet not been renewed. Then the people in the church began to sing Herbert's well-known hymn . . .

> Throw away Thy wrath!
> Throw away Thy rod!
> O my God
> Take the gentle path!

At dusk a Heinkel K bomber came over to tease the London *ack ack* batteries . . .

IN THE NIGHT

The white curb gave off a small dim grey line. A shape
was at my elbow.

"Dark night, Gov'ner. . . ."

"Always like this?"

"Not when the —— Jerries is tossin it down, matey."

"Been many hits around here?"

"Oh now that would tellin now wouldn't it . . . 'oo might
you be?"

"Just an American."

"Just an askin American."

"Sorry."

"The American newspipers say we ain't fightin."

"They are far away."

"Bloody bitchy white of 'em tellin us 'ow to fight."

"We'll wake up."

"Tike this 'ere block. Matt Oen's young un, he died 'e did in Africker . . . in a tank 'e did . . . a bloody grease spot he become . . . and our 'Enry . . . he's in Singapore and down with fever all the time . . . and 'is lungs not of the best . . . and there is Bess Simonds whose old man got done up in Norway, in one of them there raids what seems such good fun when you gits to read of it. . . . And me, bloody bugger goin on fifty-five, I am, where 'ave I been these last ten nights but marching with me gimpy feet with the blasted 'Ome Guards to here from Manchister. . . . So England ain't fightin . . . is sitting still, lettin others do it! Tell 'at to the dead ones and the widers and orphants. . . . Bloody . . . bloody 'ell!!!!"

Chapter 18

A SEA OF TROUBLE

J OE *and Grace are no longer living in a cheap London flat
with a little dog called Tea Rag. Joe is wearing Navy blue
and is second in command of the mine sweeper* Two X, *out
of the Naze of Colchester; patrolling the West and East
Friesians and digging safe channels in the mine fields for
coming commando killers of Germans.* . . .

There is a wet icy hell of white water and blue mist out

*there and the fish eat very well. Grace drives a dirty tan
Bentley, usually full of flying men going back and forth on
their leave from secret bomber fields. Tea Rag has become
a father, "And the rich Americans"—writes Grace—"are
crawling home to the Union League Club to die in the odor
of Yale drinking songs . . ."*

PART OF A LETTER FROM JOE TO CHICO
(delayed by censors)

Our luck didn't hold all the time. The *Two X* couldn't
always slip away. It happened like this: The Jerries have a
cruiser called by us the *Rat*.

Three hours before dusk the *Rat* signalled us to stand by
and await a boarding party. *Two X* was well turned, making
away and the triple expansion cylinders had just become used
to a fast tune when the *Rat's* shell came clattering and tore
into the forward collision bulkhead and killed two galley
tikes. A tall column of black smoke went up against the
sky in the drifting forms of a direct hit. The Cockney—our
Old Man—called hell and high water to witness his rape
and we leaned over and waited for things to catch up with us.

II

Two X could make twelve knots. She did fifteen now. But
the *Rat*, according to *Jane's Fighting Ships,* admitted a speed
of seventeen and it looked like twenty to us.

The *Rat* had the range again and was closing in fast, cutting the seas like a tailor cuts cloth. *Two X* tucked her funnel low in the pounding scud, and, with high-pitched screams
of the blowers forcing air into the furnaces, she spun ahead,
her flanks white with salt and us packing our overside kits.
She ate into the sea on the lee rail, shouting back at the

wind in her struts, and the vibrations of the racing twin
propellers were pounding her headlong into the rollers as
she zigzagged to keep out of the teeth of the new, rifled steel
gun on the *Rat's* deck. A prudent ship is never too boisterous
a wench at a time like this, but we had rum issued and tossed
away our lead-covered log and code books and waited.

The *Rat* threw in a bigger shell. Cockney barked an order
and the aft deck crew ran forward and pulled stiff canvas
off a shape and got the muzzle of the six-inch gun bolted to
the fo'ard planks, set at maximum, and the gun pointer, Old
Hell of Jutland, leered into the telescope sights, the brass
shell went in, the breech locked, Old Hell held the cross-
hairs on the cruiser and the deck gun went *Bammmmm-
siiiiiiii!* a hiss whammed across the sea and the gun recoiled
to breech, the hot smoking brass case fell into the sea and a
new shell went home and we held our breath. Old Hell
shifted the hair-lines, growled, the gun hooted again and
happy curses hallowed as the *Rat's* halliards dragged into the
sea. A hit! Nothing damaged, but her signal flags dangled
now like socks, hanging distractingly. I sat down on the deck
and fingered my life belt and far off mist came up fast.

Then *Two* X got it!

III

A shell, madder than all the others, came singing in and
ate past the paint-covered rust of the plated hull and it
whistled and churned its way into the engine room, shrieked
and exploded and I hated to think of down there. A racking,
piercing note re-echoed, tearing the guts out of the ship. It
was as if all the Jerry hate of our world were there.

The thrust blocks, caught in movement, were jerked out
like steel weeds and were broken like pipe stems and the
stokers—poor bastards—inhaled their own steam and died

suddenly in reprehensible postures. The rubber-set sea valves blew out like tea pots popping and the centrifugal bilge pumps, for good reason, went into death rattles as men boiled pink in seconds and a hell of steel and steam and red hot patent winches rained down on us and the sea and through space.

There was a great cracking and groaning, a tearing, breaking and a sound like mad horses on Bank Holiday. The engineer came up on deck, threw down his cotton waste and stood nailed with awful stiffness of fear as death, rained below, and the engines fell over his men. Life was snuffed out so fast that maybe there was no intense consciousness of the purpose of life. He looked at me and said: "Bitched for good—*what?*"

IV

Cockney swayed on his bridge as he heard the staccato rattle that meant that the connecting shaft had jammed and buckled and I got some men to lay hose lines. Then the twin screws jerked and there was a twist as the starboard screw fell off and went down ten fathoms to slip by astonished fish, I suppose, and rest a long time. Old Hell reached for the gun again but it hung uprooted, its muzzle pointed to a better heaven, and smoke, flames and screams and curses washed over each other and us. The *Rat* came on, guns reloaded, for the kill—almost laughing at us.

Cockney cut his steam, rammed the bronze wheel around, bellowed the remaining crew to the hand pumps and we were in a neat mess. Hull crushed in, steam gone, engines junk and no sign of help (not that we expected any with land based Jerry bombers already streaking over the lead sky).

The *Rat* moved swift like a rodent for the prey held for it by a mean sea. We waited. We had a calm crew.

Two X drifted, her deck and bridge a shameful sight, her inners still faintly struggling, frantically retching as her steam grew cold—then colder. Her inners settled down in the pong of broken steel. Sluggishly she rolled in the troughs of the seas and then like a sick barnyard animal, she moved and I swear she shivered like a bull at a butchering.

Cockney bent over the dim lighted binnacle. Old Hell, with the frayed end of three feet of old wire cable, kept

beating time as the crew worked at the blistering hand pumps. "Pump, you sea scuds, you Limehouse pub-crawling sailors!"

V

Old Hell cursed when he saw the life-boats hanging in fragments from their bent davits and winked at me. Then we drifted in silence except for the panting of the men at the pumps and the gurgle of dirty, oily water. Then there was the scream of a stoke-hole hand who had been mashed against a fire door and it sounded very high pitched. But he couldn't be reached with a Stillson wrench or a gag.

Suddenly the deck tilted—very suddenly—and then the sharp, acid bite of more shelling came whamming with sinister wallop across the sea. *Two X* seemed to explode, bolt by bolt, into a red mist. Fire and burning wet steel whirled around and a black cloud, shaped like a naked fat lady, hung over the ship and then broke apart in the wind (like a glass ghost under a brick) and after that we were all very wet. . . .

The ship splintered, shook and tilted more, tilted beyond her safe limitations and the silver edge of the sea came knifing across the deck, splashed below by the ton. The lee rail dipped under, and thousands of tons of green-white water poured into the hatches.

VI

Now die, ship, shouted Old Hell crazy as a coot. The last shell hit well forward. It was the death blow, red, and acid heat over the sea. Bulwark plates gave like paper bags. Every part of the ship had its own special death sound, scream, grunt or howl. The struts, keel plates, steel deck stringers, diamond plates, iron junk, brass, plankings, all broke their old serene hold on each other and in the slackness of death the ship shivered and became, not a living planned unit of steel and steam and sailors' skill, but just old torn iron and chaos and sea rust. Long lines of rivets pulled out (popping like billiard balls falling into a barrel). Line after line, flapping open big seams and great columns of steam rose up when the last live boiler was invaded by the salt water. Then an iron deck blew open huge gashing lips, with puffing shouts, as the air pressure under weight of rising waters became more than the windy old harridan of a ship could stand. We knew this was *it*.

The cruiser *Rat* had stopped its mean, meditative strides and tossed three cables' length away, watching the death, its hooked crosses gloating.

Two X roared now with a sudden hate at the thought of death, and huge cylinders rolled against leaking, exasperated walls and the thrust blocks charged mashing from side to side pulling the boat apart (like Victor Hugo's cannon—remember?) as they moved in the deadly clatter. A thousand heavy tools, joints, machines, doors, plates, rattled around and as the last bolt of the many shafted engines tore loose and they fell through the bottom of the ship, she heeled well over and began to sink, arse first, and I threw rafts over the side, and the wet oily bottom of *Two X,* all red lead and rust and green weed and shellfish and dock swill gleamed for a moment in the cold North Sea sunlight, then, shivering violently, settled. The deck gun tore loose, slid into the sea, pulling the funnels after it and sounds of tear and stress came quicker now as we jumped into the sea. Something happened in the mine magazine and a huge onion of smoke rose and fell apart and I felt cold brine in my mouth and the smoke cleared. . . .

When it did, *Two X* was gone and a hole marked the spot where the last inch of ship had suddenly been shoved under with a ghastly popping whistle, and I spun around and around and heads bobbed like coconuts at a village shy.

VII

Then there was only a widening circle of foam, a spinning series of ovals and doors and bottles washed together, and, moving away, the *Rat* ran for cover and Nazi bombers flew over us, and away. . . .

There now appeared a groaning hole in the sea. A huge spinning well that showed no bottom and sent up a sucking sound toward me and my chums. Boards, driftwood, bodies spun around and around this hole, tilted toward the spinning valve, and I felt it bite at me. I wept like a child.

Then there was a mad white burst of bubbles and hiss and a scatter as the last air in the deep-diving ship was shaken out of her somewhere below in the great sea pressures. Then quickly the waters calmed.

VIII

That's how it is, Chico. No poetry, no brave words, no glow for things done or undone. We floated for eight hours, then a trawler picked us up. Well, I go out again on *Three X* in two days. . . . Be a good chap, will you, and take Grace to a cinema and save one of the pups . . . one that looks like Lord H. . . .

DIMENSIONS OF TOMORROW

Shad Roe sat on his spine looking up at the wet sky and he looked very tired and lacked that subtle rueful humor. He was old and getting older and I noticed for the first time that the wrinkles were digging deeper, that the hair line was creeping back, fighting a rear guard action with hair tonics and a new hair-part. The man was almost ready to sit down with old age by his fireside, only there was no fireside and the time of resting was not yet. That demoniacal essential integrity of Shad Roe would never sit and rest. He debated daily with a long-toothed War Office fool.

I sat down and we lit cigarettes and I saw the pile of books at his elbow, old, well-worn books full of assurances and deep convictions. I missed flashy modern trash of ambassadors, radio reporters, "experts," lady reporters in tailored pants, the rag tag and literary bob of war-happy fools; politicos, journalists and novelists all trying to write a best seller for the book clubs.

II

I said: "You are old-fashioned in your reading."

"Am I? I used to be a prodigal eater of husks. I've been around a long time, boy. I've been trying on the dimensions of tomorrow."

I pointed to the old books. "And?"

"Forget the books. They say a lot—but not enough to buoy me with old beliefs. Like everyone else I've been brooding at the things that are secretly gnawing at our world; the one we were born in, lived in, are now seeing in danger."

"That's a lot of thinking to do—sober."

"I'm being thumped and goosed by doctors. I am not drinking for a week. We today, Chico—men like you and me—who still love, like, enjoy a lot of free things—we have a damned bad psychosis."

"Have we?"

"It's not Hitler's armies or the Jap ships we fear. Oh, no —wars have rolled us back before, time has beaten us bloody many times. There *is* a perverted moral strength we see about these new monsters that makes us wonder if our older political systems have been so rotted by politicos and rich families and oil and flivver kings, that we wonder, can it survive?"

"Yes, I suppose that's what worries us. The scum that has sold out Magna Carta and Jefferson."

"We call ourselves Christians and do not even try to act like Christ. We call ourselves democrats and yet neither the Negroes nor the Lady Clivedens and the Rockefellers are true democrats. One group can't understand it, the other twists its purpose to the making of money or social position."

III

"None of that is news, Shad Roe."

"Democracies really fear the full strong power behind the forces Hitler can and has brought forth. He has something that we have not found *yet*. A full working machine. Forgetting its evil, forgetting its perversion, counting results—it works. We still creak. They are young, they say. We are old. They say they are the future and that we are the past. The wrong is that we listen to such talk and shiver instead of going back to Tom Paine, John Brown and Andrew Jackson. Our morale is sapped and we stand and watch dividends, loud mouths, Congressmen, the House of Lords play at politics and hog-calling and mountain singing."

"It isn't just that."

IV

"We lack one great aim, one great drive. This war is of mixed purpose, of mixed ideals, and we are scattered in our ideas and our outlooks. We need one goal, one purpose, and we are bickering and still trying to say it will all come out in the end just dandy."

"Maybe it will," I said.

"No. We must find more than a newsreel meeting on the high seas, we must find more than screen writers in Majors' uniforms, making dull motion pictures of flags waving. We have lost much of our first ardor and we must replace it. Our religious men have failed. They have offered us holy ashes and oil and great piles of stone with electric organs and a lot of talk about another, happier world. I like *this* world, and I want it clean and happy. I look bad in wings and I can't play a harp. Hell is more to my taste—but while waiting, I want to enjoy this one."

"I see."

"No, you don't. To you I'm an old man reading old books. Moral standards are lost to us today. I've tattered a few standards in my time. But I've never murdered working men, beaten mill children, broken bodies on the Rand or on Dearborn assembly lines. I've not lynched Negroes or burned rival oil wells, broken Jewish or Hindu noses, called pioneers 'Okie' or 'convict trash' or dwarfed a race of cockneys by underfeeding them. Democracies have done *all* that. So our moral standards must begin again on a new series of Ten Commandments. No one ever took the set Moses got seriously. We are bewildered and careless today. Our people trade their votes to Irish or fox-hunting scoundrels, and to oil or steel thieves and to the advertising lobbies of those who sell what no one really wants anyway. Do you follow me, Chico?"

"No, but go on."

V

"I mean, we can lose all our world because the little people will give up their political freedom for so-called economic security, because they no longer love us Christians, us readers of the *Times*—us lousy politicos and generals . . . They are beginning to expect our world to crack and they may want to save what they can at any cost. We lack Lincolns, Gladstones and Christs."

"I follow you now."

"These books you think I should put away, and should read instead modern amateur ambassadors, and ghost-written diaries of trained seals with news services, of Harvard wits and damn fools dancing in uniform, with little war fronts written up as if they were Verdun. . . . No, I read the old books. They are my diagnoses of doom; *unless* we do something. We do not need mere indictments of our installment civilization, but the whole truth which these books have been telling us for a long time. Ibsen—not the arty summer-theatre-man in cheesecloth and summer society scratching its insect-bitten legs—but the series of dramas that indict modern society for its evils, its sins, its failure to live upright on two feet like honest men, rather than mere animals twitching in their mulch."

"Yes. Ibsen saw it all a long time ago. But so did Proust, so—even—did Balzac. Every free writer worth his salt knew that he had a theme there but you know damn well unless you lard it with sexual love and details of bedrooms, no one reads you. Our free education system is geared only to produce tabloid and confession readers."

"Tolstoy—he repudiated society, saw the symptoms of rot appear in the civilization that Rothschilds, Morgans, du Ponts were so happy about."

It was beginning to rain. The small fire smoked on its warm bricks. Shad Roe closed his eyes.

"Well, to most of the world Tolstoy was only a Russian in a muff," I said.

"What about Alfred Lord Tennyson—he had a beaver, too. All his life he was obsessed with the disintegration of nineteenth century Christian England. Read his poem—not those about knights, and pale girls and their maidenheads . . .

'The fortress crashes from on high,
The brute earth lightens to the sky,
And the great Aeon sinks in blood.' "

VI

"You can't use Tennyson—he's the god of the Nice Nellies."

"All right, Chico. I'll use Thomas Hardy. He looked about him and was sure this world of ours had sold out to greed and its meanness was not the job of a conscious Being. He invented something, years before Freud, that is a very popular sport now. Remember him writing of 'The coming universal wish not to live'?"

"No, I don't."

Shad Roe fumbled in a big scrapbook.

"Let me read you what a lot of people said about our times and what they would lead to unless we took back our birthright. None agree too much. But they divide into two groups. Total nothing, and total everything:

"A Roman sibyl said: 'There shall be no end to war in this world. They all shall slay one another.' Victor Hugo on the twentieth century: 'War will be dead, the scaffold will be dead, animosity will be dead, but man will live.' Lenin: 'Socialism, putting an end to classes, will thereby put an end to the State.' Chekhov: 'Do you know that in three or four hundred years all the earth will become a flourishing garden. And Life will then be exceedingly easy and comfortable.' Hitler in 1920: 'Today brute force can conquer only by assuming a socialist, a revolutionary cloak. *Never* can Germany win a war if England is fighting actively on the opposing side. Only by ideologically destroying it from *within* can Germany conquer Europe. By brute force alone—never!' America's prophet, John Ballou Newbrough, prophesies that 'there will be a great revolution in the U.S. circa 1947, and that all nations will be demolished and all the earth be thrown open to all people to go and come as they please.' Tolstoy: 'No rational man . . . can help seeing that there is no practical way out; that it is impossible to devise any alliance or organization that can save us from the destruction into which we are uncontrollably rushing.' The most magnificent prophets are still the Jews. Isaiah and Ezekiel and the author of the *Book of Revelation*."

VII

The rain was driving down in great force. It spit against the windows and foamed in the gutters.

"All right, Shad Roe," I said. "You have made your point. Now what?"

"We must be realists to win. We must realize that for good or bad . . . and I use the terms, like Spinoza, with distaste . . . *good* and *bad* can often mean anything or something from *where* you are and *what* you are, but good or bad we must understand that the Russian Revolution began what we are still fighting about—the first of a series of social protests—that the First World War is still going on, and it's a mistake to call this one Number Two. The year 1914 was the serious crack in our civilization and if we had not been blind or had the brains of a generation killed off, we would have seen it. The second tear in our silver envelope of business-as-usual was the bloody brutal Nazi tribal uprising. We must take off our blinders and think right and think true and think fast. Speed is suddenly important. Hitler's killer mob has lifted the lid from the mistakes of man since the Dark Ages."

"And?"

"We can no longer support a fat skin, we can no longer turn the other way when reaction, when power and political hogwash and business madness ruins us. The good times, the mad times, the years of panics and bull markets, can no longer swing back by themselves into years of slow social reform. This is no time for slow cycles, first of reaction and then of some reform; panic and plenty in turn."

"I begin to understand."

"American and English conservatism; the foolish days of Hoover and Harding, the periods of Chamberlains and Bank of England holidays were powerful forces in their day—that felt they could handle the steering wheel for us. But no more. Those days and times are over. We are now standing around naked and if we want to walk on two free legs we must have more than a Better Business Bureau, Buy British slogans and two chickens in every Ford car. Call it Christ, Lenin, Buddha, Henry George, Einstein, Tolstoy, but give us honest hope."

"Give it a name."

VIII

Shad Roe got up to find an old pipe; he did, and lit it. He stood puffing and then sat down and looked into the pipe bowl. "It has no name yet, Chico. Some might say nationalism, some collectivism, some pacifism . . . I don't call it any of that. I see a proper and honest and full use of all resources of our civilization from Shakespeare to the du Ponts' last shirt.

"I don't want to hear it called collectivism, brotherly love, Christian Science, yoga or socialism or any other motto. All I want is *our* weapon, strong as Hitler's, hard as his *panzers*, cruel as his Gestapo, to save us for ourselves and from ourselves.

"For in fighting the Nazis we are fighting our black selves. All the meanness we have done, all the dirty work of Empire and holding-company, all the slimy fat-robed snobbery of church and bank, all the speed-ups and dividend digging, all the evil in man, all the race and creed hate and restricted golf club and cricket field is what we are fighting really in the Nazi.

"He has geared a whole savage tribal uprising to the gadgets we sold for money. He has won so far and will go on winning because we showed him how to organize for profit, for power, for stock exchange and factory winnings. And he is bright enough to turn our ideas against us, because that was all we ever offered him—gadgets—Rockefeller gas and U.S. Steel built into Jap bombers.

"Lindberghs, Wheelers and Hearsts by throwing dust helped him to strangle Poland and Holland and France, and half our world is gone for good."

"That's a little too strong for me," I said.

"Not all Americans think like you, Chico. Ever read Lewis Mumford?" He picked up his scrapbook again.

"Some."

" 'If our free democratic world is saved, it will be saved not just by machines and guns, but by our capacity to produce a higher type of human being, whose will and purpose are superior to that of the enemy.

" 'Big machines are of no use if they are run by little men. During the last two generations, in particular, the community has been paralyzed by the fact that our material organizations have outrun our moral and intellectual capacity to make good use of them. In their technical refinement, our machines have often approached perfection; but no similar development has been visible in the education of men. On the contrary: the typical human product of our time, especially among the leaders of our society, is either a paranoiac personality, warped by delusions of grandeur and an insatiable lust for power, or a split personality, in which the intellectual, the emotional and the practical sides are divided into watertight compartments. The first type tends to be destructive; the second, trivial or impotent.' "

"I remember that now," I said, watching the rain.

" 'The humanities and science are not in inherent conflict but have become separated in the twentieth century. Now their essential unity must be re-emphasized, so that twentieth century multiplicity may become twentieth century unity. One technique will be to acquaint students with the great masters of reality, not politicians, businessmen and economists, but Sophocles, Shakespeare, Isaiah, Dostoevski, St. Paul . . .' "

IX

"And so?" I asked. "Tell me—I'm leaving for the Middle East next week."

"That's all. I'm finished talking and reading for a while. Let's go down and have some ale."

"Your doctor said . . ."

"Damn my doctor! He's like our politicos. They write slogans and go away without doing anything about it. If I'm ill, cure me. If I'm dying, kill me off and let better things —like daisies—grow out of my eye sockets."

"Let's have the ale. . . ."

Shad Roe hunted his burberry and got his arm through it and pulled a disrespectful hat over his brow. "Let me quote one more thing, then drag me out of here:

'Poor man, what art? A tennis ball of error,
A ship of glass tossed in a sea of terror,
Issuing in blood and sorrow from the womb,
Crawling in tears and mourning to the tomb;
How slippery are thy paths, how sure thy fall,
How art thou nothing, when thou art most of all!' "

HOT COFFEE

At the airport the mist was heavy and the plane was late. A very pretty girl was heating coffee in the chill hangar and we stood around holding hot mugs in our numb fists. Not a light showed on the field.

The girl took my cup.

"Have another."

"No thanks. Glum place, isn't it?"

"Not so bad . . . they have dances here once a week for the air officers . . ."

"You like to dance?"

"Adore it . . . But it's bad for me."

"In what way?"

"The first time I went there I met a man . . . and married him."

"I see."

"A week later he was shot down over the Channel in flames."

"Too bad."

"I stayed away for a while . . . but there aren't many girls. I went to another dance . . . well there I was a week later a new bride. This one never came back from a Kiel raid, and later we got word he was killed when his plane ran into heavy *flak*."

"Airmen have a hard job."

"I haven't been to a dance for three months . . . but they keep asking me."

"Will you go?"

"Well I can't spend the war making coffee . . . can I?"

"No, of course not . . ."

The field suddenly glowed for a moment, the white lights died out, and rain beat against new red and green lights. Thunder dissolved into a huge flying shape and the big three-motored bat ran across the semi-dark field.

"There is your plane," said the girl.

"Thanks for the coffee."

A tall thin man in the slate blue of the RAF came over and took the girl's hand.

"Tip-top American music tonight, old girl . . . what say?"

The girl looked at me and I turned my back, picked up my bag and went out into the rain. I looked back once. He was a very handsome fellow and he smiled very well and had a careless way of draping himself over the coffee-making machine.

I suppose by now the girl is a widow several times over. I used to think about her . . . and once I wrote a letter to Grace asking her to look up the girl and find out how she was. But I never mailed the letter. There are so many loose threads you leave unwound behind you in a world at trouble. But you think about it and wonder . , . and that's the curse of a story teller with a liking for simple everyday people. . . .

Book Five

THE DEVIL IN ASIA

Chapter 19

ORDEAL BY AIR

Over the Roman Sea he could see the nervous convoys moving, and often other airplanes besides his—maybe hostile, but he didn't worry too much for he had been through a great deal and was very tired and was going to inspect the outposts of Empire. And Chico was still young enough to have left in his veins some of the bigoted prose poison, (so well written by Kipling). Yes, the East still attracted him. By morning he no longer felt any fear of the sky. Air travel, Shad Roe had once told him, was aphrodisiac and emetic. . . .

PORTRAIT OF AN ENGLISHMAN

The huge plane was two hours late out of star-covered Malta and in the purple heat of the night we dropped a pontoon into the Red Sea and had to limp back into Port Said for repairs. From then on we flew along the burning, blinding Arabian Sea with the taste of fear and disaster always with me, and the heat was at the season when it also flew high, and drummed in soaring fever against all life. Even the glaring water under the plane's great wing-spread seemed to boil like molten steel; steel that heaved like damp fire. . . . The pilot was very bored with it all.

II

We hit a mean black line storm as we neared Ceylon, rose above it and went on. I didn't care any more after that. My nerves were numb. I just sat tight and wondered about the seven mad moments of war and life (that are said by teacup

readers to twist out our destiny). I was going to Ceylon to interview some canned-soup baron, or tea king, or traveling chain-store cake-baker—I forget now—and to cable what he thought on war, deep-sea fishing and the white man's prestige beyond the seas. (I had always felt it would have been more sporting and much more important to ask about canned soup, tea or cake-baking.) The sea was numb and I was tired of looking at its dull tossing face; the face of a sinister idol

that really had nothing much to say unless you are Joseph
Conrad. . . .

There was only one other civilian person traveling with
me, besides the pilots and the blue-eyed steward. My fellow
traveler was a tall, red-headed Englishman, the old-fashioned,
Somerset Maugham kind, with a clear, protuberant, public-
school eye, broad shoulders and a slim slit of a mouth with
hard corners. The heat had worked into him, too, I could see
—even if his deep Vandyke-brown skin spoke of long years
under a strong sun and trying to carry on an Empire deader
than he thought.

He had come aboard at Malta and had sat most of the
way out, so far, looking out of the window or reading a
small, red book with many yellowed, dog-eared pages, reading
as if he were trying Greek for the first time. It was a cook
book. Even when we lost our pontoon he had only whistled
and kept his place in the book with a strong brown thumb
and rubbed his nails on the window glass. But now the heat
had him, too, and he was wilting, dignity and all, as fast as
the starch went out of his collar. I was rather that way myself and we melted and sat and rubbed.

III

I don't speak first to strange Englishmen any more, or
dangle my school key on its solid gold chain in front of
their eyes and ask them "how's tricks?" Now I wait for them
to throw in the first pleasant word. The cook-book-reader
had so far shown no interest in me, the plane or the trip and
he sat and read of scarlet Thessaly pepperheads, of the rare
wonder of Perigord truffles; and wiped heat haze off his
brow, or rubbed with a firm thumb on the prickly heat that
blossomed on his neck like a red-hot chain.

I was sitting, wondering why I didn't go home for keeps,

when a proper public-school voice—the kind no American believes in off the stage (with its elongated vowels and stressed consonants) asked me if I'd like a snifter and wasn't the heat bloody awful.

Amazed, I turned and there was the Englishman offering me a nest of silver cups and a bottle of Scotch with the right kind of label; his red puffy eyes crinkled into invitation.

"Thanks—don't mind if I do," I said, and I took a little silver cup and poured myself three fingers and drank it. The Englishman put aside the cook book and smiled at me and I saw he had a wonderful smile, the kind young girls like (Englishmen can be charming once you crack their shell but life has more things to do than crack shells).

"My name is Smith-Brasil. You're going East, what?"

I admitted it. It was too hot to say more. We each had another Scotch and then two more. Fine stuff. I moved over to his seat and we watched Ceylon come up over the sea-scape—yellow-green in the sun, orange-purple in the shade and very like the travel posters of it. The plane hummed on and its shadow followed on the water below at a steady pace equal to our own. We drank to it and soon Smith-Brasil tossed the cook book on the floor and kicked his long legs about and scratched his belly.

"Damn stuff was the only thing I've had to read since England. I'm a proper bookworm and I need them like a drug out in Ceylon."

"Planter?"

"Tea—thousands of fields of it—and what for?"

"Market lousy?"

"No blasted market at all—anywhere. No ships. The whole world hit by war. How's America taking it? All right?"

I nodded and decided to change the subject. "Have a good time in London?" I asked, playing Sherlock Holmes with his luggage tags and admiring the shapes pig-pelt and bull-hide can take.

"Oh, jolly," he said, as if he weren't sure but felt he had to carry on in front of a stranger. "Some of it was school-boy stuff and a lot of it was just a series of tea fights. I'll not go back there again. I'll stick to Ceylon and a few shoots into India after tiger. I have a new Smith Super 300 bore. But England belongs to another age for me. Been away too long. Staying here long?"

"No. Just a touch-and-go interview."

"Come again soon—lots to see—lots to do on Ceylon." It didn't sound like the usual polite invitation. I think he really would have enjoyed having me in tow for a while. He looked down on the sea and his face was twisted in thought (as if his face muscles were unused to the process and what he was thinking disagreed with him). He tossed his head sideways and looked at the time, strapped to his red wrist, and then smiled lightly all over his face, raw rubbed—but as if his soul weren't really in it. He picked up the Scotch again and scratched his armpits and grunted in relief.

"Ceylon. Devil of a strange place," he said suddenly. "Never was built for white men. Too lush—too humid. Things grow too fast and take on strange shapes and I'm not telling you any punk-scented junk out of an adventure magazine. I mean something happened. Private, personal matter. Details—bore you—but it showed me that white men here find themselves thinking like the natives, seeing things the way they do, following their procedures and codes, and then suddenly know that you need a trip to England. Easy place, Ceylon, to go potty in. Very."

I held up a small silver cup and the sun struck it and a gleam of highlights ran around its brim and I didn't bother about his trite remarks.

"Pour again," I said. "I think the natives pity us whites

now. We have lost face too often and lack balance and the Fifth Column gossips say you British fight too many brilliant, rear-guard actions."

"Damn the natives. Half devils—half children. Who said that?"

"Kipling."

"So he did. Great man, *that*."

He poured into my cup again and the drink ran into the cup with little slopping sounds. The bottle was half empty and the plane dipped for landing and Ceylon came up green, wet and too fast, to meet us. My traveling companion dug his fists into the padded arms of his chair and watched the silver and green and brown strips of good earth grow larger. His mouth twitched but his teeth were tight together and his poor, torn skin grew redder.

The plane tipped on a sharper angle and banked to the left; I saved the Scotch just in time.

IV

Ceylon is full of words like *dhow* and *tiffin* that your friends once wrote back from their round the world tour, and I didn't like it. My soup king was still three days off by steamer and time hung balanced heavy over me. Dullness, heat, natives and rumors knocked against each other and jarred our nerves. And a Charlie Chaplin character played the hotel piano all day long. . . .

I went down to the hotel bar and began to test the theory that rye highballs are cooling—no matter how high the heat. The bar was long and cool and was kept polished by tall, handsome black men in colored sheets and a line of serious drinkers: planters, travel-book writers and *pukka wallahs,* did a great deal of elbow bending and rubbing of their heat-rashed hide. The long green shades and the spinning fans

gave a clean comfort, and there was even a stone carving of
a little figure of Pu-L'ai, the god of lechery (surely the management didn't know *that*).

I was sipping and just wondering about the state of things
when someone slapped me on the shoulder and called me
"chappie." I don't take well to "chappie" so I turned quickly
and it was Smith-Brasil, looking very neat in white drill, very
tall, trim and shaved and healed and ready to bear the burden of heat, war, Kipling, unsold tea and a few drinks.

"Have one on me," I said, moving over to make room at
the busy bar. Drink is a medical treatment in the East—at
least, all *goddamn* it and force themselves to carry on against
their livers with tinkling glasses. Smith-Brasil looked very fit
in his stengah shifter and I wondered how he would do in
Hollywood. Sam Goldwyn would love his type. . . .

"Just one," said Smith-Brasil, pulling out a Faberge cigarette case and offering me a corktip and bending a smile

over me as he lit it. He was glad to see me. "My car is outside and I'm off to the hills. Leaving soon?"

I shook my head and pulled on the damp cigarette. "No luck. I've got to wait three days. You're looking fit."

"Proper," he said, holding a fresh match under my cigarette and setting fire to it again. His strong brown hand shook a bit and he watched the match burn to a char in his fingers and then he looked at me and I can't tell you *how*— just a look with some strain of a plea in it and I liked the man suddenly, forgave him his caste system. "How about being my guest until you need to get back here? It's grand in the hills this time of year. Ever eat Lobster *à la Portugaise?*"

I shook my head. "Never. But can your cook prepare a *chaud-froid* of chicken and Ceylon crayfish?"

Smith-Brasil patted my shoulder. "Let's go."

We had two more rounds first and I liked him fine. Gin pahits do that to you.

V

Smith-Brasil drove, and he drove an old 1910 Rolls, and he drove as if in ten minutes they were going to take him out and hang him (hanging might have been better on the nerves). There was no road, no path, no markers. There was a streak, a rolling skid-making rut, studded like fruit cake with big rocks (looking like raisins) and danger no end, and I'm not trying to make an adventure of this. I dislike adventures. . . .

It was a lush wet land stewing under a high wafer of a red sun and there were high wool-gathering clouds but no shade. Soon we left behind the little gardens, the gaunt bones of old fallen temple roofs and the plodding coolies, big with many loads, their ribs flapping over tired hearts. . . .

Ahead there was a hum—a roar—as if mad bees were in meeting and the high hill seemed never to end and then the car was braked quickly at the lip of a deep descent into a valley of foam and sound, and far down a river boiled over among many shaggy rocks after making the high jump of a waterfall, a fall that was like a silver apron two hundred feet high. A long, narrow, unwilling bridge went across the river in one hop-skip-and-jump of fear and it shook like a thread in the breeze. I have never seen a more dainty little bridge. Or a more ugly river to pass over.

The heavy car started downhill, skidding almost sideways, and we came slowly to the bridge, the silver lady on the hood holding her skirts. Smith-Brasil held the wheel steady in his strong brown fingers and I looked up at him and his brow was beaded in sweat and his open mouth sucked air from between tight teeth the way a land-trapped trout does. I grabbed for the wheel but his elbow shoved me back against the seat and I wondered if he were sick.

"What's the matter, man?" I asked. "You look ghastly!"

"Nothing—nothing, really."

The heavy car hit the first planks of the bridge. Hundreds of feet below, the jagged teeth of the rocks tossed river spume over their sharp snags and waited for a bite at us and I wondered what goddamn melodrama I was part of.

The panting Englishman swung the car in line with the thin bamboo bridge rails and stepped on the petrol so that we crossed with the nervous speed of a cat in a fearful hurry. Smith-Brasil looked ahead through the boiling river mist and spoke softly from the side of his mouth, his voice very soft and calm and I wondered if it was an act to impress me.

"Terrible thing happened here six months ago. Terrible."

"I can well imagine."

Smith-Brasil kept his eyes on the oncoming jade-green jungle. "My wife's car ran off this bridge during a storm, right through the rails. Never recovered the body. Horror gets me every time I cross here."

"Sorry," I said, looking down over the rails. "I didn't know."

The big man beside me sobbed and choked back a cry and the car had gripped the wet clay at the bridge and it roared ahead with no slowing of pace and I felt a fool trapped in a tropical play about sex and passion under palm trees.

"Broke me all up," said the Englishman, feeling he must explain his show of emotion in such bad taste. "Took all of three months in England to make me feel a little alive again. Tried to sell out here—but no takee, these days. This seeing it again—sorry to trouble you—personal affairs, I know . . ."

I reached for a pocket in my trenchcoat. "How would some real brandy—French stuff—go now?"

"Rather hit the spot," he said and began to cry. (To hear a full-grown man cry is a horrible thing and cheapens an emotional scene.) High in the hills a storm was brewing and I could smell mignonette among the china-blue hydrangea bushes we were passing and behind us, over the river, *reine claude* clouds began to gather and soon out of nowhere a hard rain began to speak very loud against the canvas top of the Rolls. The trees tossed like unskilled dancers and full sheet-sized panes of water were pushed aside by the busy wipers on our windshield. How it came down! (Overdone stage effects, and a character out of *Sadie Thompson* at my side.)

The brandy didn't last long. The empty bottle skidded across the wet grass and crashed against the warped bole of a laburnum tree and broke into shattered glass shards. It was a hell of a lot to go through for a dish of chicken and crayfish, fond as I am of them, and I suddenly hated this slobbering Englishman out of cheap fiction. Then I liked him again; because he hadn't gone stout fella—chin-and-tail-up, on me.

VI

Three days later I was back in my hotel bar, drinking Stait stingers with the same group of beet-red Hollywood-looking sahibs, and waiting to be admitted to my soup king's suite. I had had a wonderful time in the hills. Three full days of reverie and lethargy among the swaying emerald tea plants. Up in the clearness of hill and sky and air a man could think out things (if he wanted to) and I had almost made up my mind to chuck the East and go home and write a travel book. Everybody else had.

Smith-Brasil was a perfect host and the food—even the *chaud-froid*—had been above par, and we drank nothing but beer for a while. Cool beer, iced to a chill, deep down a hundred feet of old temple well; while we sat around in a big stone and bamboo house hung with many Turcoman objects and embroideries and talked. Native servants in Javanese sarongs tiptoed around and at night they sat around fires in the yard—giggling at us.

VII

Once we went hunting, hunting a rare animal with beaters and guns—but I don't know just what kind of animal it was, as we never caught up with it. And later the war news on the wireless was breathless.

VIII

I had just finished brushing my teeth and was pulling tight the belt of the borrowed Afghan dressing gown, when the split bamboo door of my room was thrown open and Smith-Brasil came into the room.

He stood directly under the lime-yellow light cast by the only oil lamp swaying in the room and he swayed, too. He looked into the shadows of the room and said to me:

"Everything normal?"

I got into bed and tried not to grin. I wasn't tight but I was sure Smith-Brasil was.

I got up on one elbow and said: "Boss, there ain't no one here but us chickens."

He rubbed his face hard with a brown hand and went out suddenly, carefully closing my door behind him and I wondered what ailed the English these days. Next morning we parted, the best of friends.

SIX MONTHS OF TRAVEL NOTES

India is all they say it is. I am not going to write much about it. I think the English are wrong, the Hindoos are wrong, the little man in the white sheet is wrong, the heat, dirt, disease, red-faced English polo players, dung-covered holy men, filth, mad gods, holy cows, lousy monkeys . . . I think they are all wrong. I have no cure, I have no real ideas on the subject. I shall write nothing important about India.

HOLY MAN

He lived on the border and played both sides against each other. Like most holy men he was a fraud, but unlike most, in other lands, he didn't drive a Buick or play bridge or ask donations for an oil heater or a rose window.

He stood in dirty rags and showed white teeth in a filthy pock-marked face and dared you to pass him by.

"You no give?"

"I no give."

"You bags says New York label."

"You can read?"

"I go Oxford, once long ago, as servant to polo ponies belonging to my master, big boss now in Cawnpore and Lucknow."

I almost said some of my best friends were Oxford men.

"I once go New York, cook on hemp boat. Very fine job."

"As good as begging as a holy man?"

"Oh no . . . this very grand job. Me wait twenty year for father to die."

"The old firm carries on?"

"My son he stand here some day."

"Even if Japs come?"

"Japs no come if English no let them."

"You like English?"

"English good for India. Keep masses alive, keep bad rulers down, keep always excitement going on."

I asked about the little man in his sheet and his party.

"They deep think fellas maybe. They big fools too . . . they like see names in paper. Maybe they love everybody . . . maybe not . . . but they never be at Oxford with polo ponies . . . only to study . . . they never cook on tramp boat, they never smear dung on face and stand in sun begging. They no live real life . . . they no understand hardness, cruel thing life is. They too full clean sheets, great ideas, too many poems . . . I real India. You give small silver coin?"

"I give small copper coin."

"Ah . . . you damn smart fella too."

I didn't feel very smart. . . .

RIVER MAN

He was all bones and no meat and he pushed a heavy oar and took small fish from a fair fruit-green river with big horny hands.

"Me fish. Some day good . . . some day bad. Some year eat . . . some year fill belly with mud. Some time live, some-time family die. No read, no write. Me twenty and ten, me have six children live, four dead. No land, no tool. Boat be-long village banker. Man in sheet who drink goat? No under-stand what he say. Poor man, poor. . . ."

Chapter 20

AN EMPIRE

MULLAHS again preaching holy war read the 5th verse, 9th chapter of the *Koran:*

And when the sacred months are past, kill those who join other gods with God wherever you shall find them; and seize them and slay them and lay in wait for them with every kind of ambush. . . .

And the Fifth Column said the English, as usual, were sipping tea and downing brandy on the houseboats on the Nile, while the troops sat in sand storms dreaming of ale, and everyone said the desert was no place to fight, and a man named Rommel was a fool to try it, and anyway they would beat him because he was no gentleman and they were cutting off his supplies and pouring castor oil and fish oil into the wells and the jolly old war would end before he had a chance to move.

It was like that all through the Middle East while the Greeks were overrun and the slogan *too late and too little* was almost replacing the old one, *the English lose all battles but the last one.*

Rommel was happy to hear both slogans.

II

There were little men from Nippon, too, hissing little monsters, very polite (each one with eyeglasses and camera attached to his navel at birth), and they spoke Fifth Column talk softly, about the colored races having had enough from Standard Oil and Vickers and the fat Dutch queen who sweated colored men on beautiful islands, *and* the colored people, the black and yellow and brown and tan listened. . . .

III

Several letters from Smith-Brasil followed me—all speaking of a great tiger hunt he was planning. I never went but I almost did. There had been a riot in India and I had flown north and put up at a native hotel, a pest bag of a place (not half as nice as the famed Black Hole of Calcutta), and I had filed my story after hanging around for three weeks and went back to my diggings in Bombay. I found a wire waiting and it was from Smith-Brasil and he was inviting me to go on a tiger hunt with some Army chappies. It was to be a real "pukka shoot" from elephants and he would tell me more as he expected to pass through Bombay in two days. The wire was two weeks old, so I've never hunted tigers. Even dead tigers scare me. . . .

IV

Then a month later, when I was in Indo-China, following an armed Jap peace mission (with tanks), I heard of an uproar caused by an Englishman being dragged off by a tiger and eaten. I got in touch with a British consul and the red-

tape and paper work on the case was fearful to behold. The
man's name was Smith-Something, they said, and they
guessed it was a tiger that got him, or perhaps a water
buffalo. Nasty affair, no?

V

So I went to see a Colonel ffolliot (small f) in charge of a
big Burma district, and he hemmed and hawed and gave
me many splash-and-sodas and nodded. Yes, it had been
Smith-Brasil. Dragged off by a tiger. Never found enough
to bury, even. Might have buried the tiger in his place if
they had caught the man-eater. Shame. Decent chappie, this
Smith-Brasil. The best die young out here. Have another.
Damn climate—only way to stay tip-top is to drink.

So that was that, and I left to cover an invasion rumor
somewhere. And that was about all I could find out about
the tiger-eaten fate of the Englishman who had been so,

kind to me at Ceylon. I was not very satisfied with the facts. I'm old-fashioned enough to like a beginning and middle and end to things—but I suppose the bright young critics of today laugh at that. Life isn't like that, really, they say— and I suppose it isn't, any more. . . .

SOLID SINGAPORE

The little yellow warped men of Nippon were stirring, and the treasures of Dearborn and Detroit and Threadneedle Street and the House of Lords were piled high around the bastions of Empire in Asia, and people were comfortable in their holdings of oil, rubber and tin, and the dividends flowed while war went on its business as usual. Chico had a cable to go and inspect Singapore and the rubber trees and the tin mines. And a fellow named Mike, whom he had once known, was getting married, and Chico had been asked to be best man.

Two hundred million pounds had made Singapore a great fortress, said the fortune tellers in the press. . . .

MICE IN THE CROWN ROOM

I was on the deck of an Arab fruit boat on the Singapore run, watching her rusting bow cut the slime-green sea, and smelling the assorted specials of rubber plantations' coolies on the foredeck, and the rotten rinds of long-gone fruit in the hull, and the Jap spies hissing over their cameras. I knew the roaches were as big as polo ponies below and that the Sumatra cook believed that tobacco juice was a food flavor as he prayed *La Allah il Allah.* . . . Two troop ships and a rusting British destroyer followed us. The Japs snapped shots.

II

On the third day I was wet and unhappy in Singapore, full of gin pahits and lies told me at the American bar. I saw no planes, few guns. The next morning, after the biggest, widest, wettest rainstorm I had ever seen and while the city was wrapped in a glove of violet mist, I hired a jaloppy for the tin mines north of Malacca. Secret bombing planes were there, everyone said. I never saw any.

III

What a land! It reeked of rain and long-molding jungle and of trees dead and dying for ages. The paths were eaten up by creepers, insects carried swords, and the drip drip of mist was everywhere. I sat in the jaloppy, watching the mold grow on my leather shoes. Then at noon the sun came out and boiled the marrow out of things, and the dreadful heat spread until my blood seemed to boil over and color the landscape a pink tint. I asked an English Major—what if the Japs came *this* way. "No one," he said, "really ever walks here."

The Bantok mines lay in a red-eroded hill, long wet crimson gashes in the pelt of the mountains. It was higher there, but the sun and fever worked their will on the logy whites and left them tanned as leather and very romantic-looking in the shade of their bamboo dwellings. I saw many natives where "no one really walked."

The purple heat of the night covered us like a wet blanket when we arrived. Six bamboo buildings on stilts stood on the banks of a silky river deep in luxuriant vegetation. Native troops in tin hats slept in tents. Behind them the cone-shaped huts of the working natives were alive with fires, the yowl of babies, the root-a-toot of hens and pigs and a dark motley of swaying dancers. There were no tanks, anti-aircraft guns or armored cars.

Mike stood on the drawbridge of his bamboo castle right where the road for rickshaws and gharries passed for Singapore. He was in a singlet and sarong, holding out a big red fist to me. Mike was thinner, harder than in his college days, with the yellow eyeballs of a black-water-fever sufferer. But his grip hadn't changed at all, nor the beef with which he always slapped a friend on the back. I took and gave a thoroughly good drubbing and knew *no* dozen Japs were a match for Mike.

"Good to see you again, Old Horse! I knew you'd come. True blue pal!"

"Crazy pal," I said, paying off the grinning shine in the jaloppy and listening to the rhythmical night clatter of the natives in a huddle under the green mangroves and nipas. "Only a soft fool would brave the heat up from Sing. Where are the defense lines?"

"What defense lines? I'm getting married."

Mike grinned, slapped me again on the back, and with an arm around me, led me to his verandah to a rattan chair. He took my sun-helmet, gave me a peg of brandy, mauled about me as if he were a mother hen bossing a chick and then stood back to get all of me into one big look (as if he expected me to be as young and lean as in our school days).

"Yes, you're getting fatter than a bank president, Old Horse. You're as vile tempered as ever but it's good to see that ugly pan of yours. Now let's have a few toasts to the old days and the shape of things to come. Forget the Jappies —they don't dare come here. Wait until you meet Fran!"

I took the cold glass he handed me and sipped.

"I gather Fran is the future Mrs. Mike."

"Right as rain," said Mike, beaming with that pride all

men have when they make fools of themselves over some woman.

"To Fran," I said, lifting my elbow again. "May the poor girl never know what she is getting."

Beyond the verandah the calm brilliance of moonlight broiled over a river spotted by the drifting *prahus* of fishing natives. Far to the east a single-lunged sports plane marred the solid night-muttering.

"You old buck," said Mike, pouring, "you still need an *ayah* when ladies are present. Come on, let's have a wash and change for dinner. But no war talk."

I gave up. "No war talk."

IV

We went around to the back under the great bamboo screen and two boys sluiced water over our heads by the pailful. Then we dressed, scented our skins with *eau de cologne* and sat down to dinner. I had to admit Mike had it down to a system. He looked neat and proper in his starched whites. The table was laid where the river breezes would do us the most good, and a tall, scarred Malay in a white jacket and Javanese sarong served us a *rystafel* (which is a hundred dishes in one and something you'll find in no cook book).

I ate and Mike talked and I have found it better to let men in love babble. As for myself, I think of Swift's line: *"There is no marriage or giving in marriage in Heaven."* I ate and listened to the wonder that was Fran, and grew warmer, and high in the hills by the light of great flares I could see the nude night-shifts at the mine. Tin was up— ships hard to get—but the digging went on. War had been good to tin. I swallowed the wine and wondered why everyone was so sure about the Japs not coming.

V

I dug a flying beetle out of my pink ice and went on with dinner. Crickets as big as sparrows were playing fiddles like mad in a rhythmic cadence on the canvas ceiling, and there was the smell of wood smoke drifting across the river and a myriad of fireflies sailed, little burning kites—there was no sense of doom in nature.

Out back the natives were still dancing to an obscure chaos of tin cans. The sports plane was no longer heard and who the hell was I to doubt the British Empire?

CLUB PEOPLE

The English Club was like a thousand clubs I had visited from Port Said to Djokjakarta. It was built like a shoe box with a huge cool porch and a long dining room with high slatted windows and a big main room with many tables, on which last year's magazines rubbed covers with old detective novels and unopened copies of scientific journals. Against one wall was the usual hardwood bar, and three scrupulously clean natives in starched white worked like galley slaves among the soda syphons, the bottles and glassware, cheerfully undermining the white man's prestige and certain of his inner organs. . . .

II

A great many people in white cottons and linens stood around chattering under the low, bug-loved lights. The men, smoking sepia cheroots, were thin and tanned and fever-marked, and the women—those who had been out here a few years—were beginning to fade into that pale, soft weakness that overtakes white women in the misty heat of the

Malay Coast along the Tropic of Cancer; and they talked
of babies, illnesses (not of lovers and death as I had expected). The Malay women in the yard sneered at them. . . .

Everyone came over to slap Mike on the back and offer
to buy him a drink in the diverse shapes being mixed. I shook
hands, bowed to the ladies and took up my place at the bar.
A tall chap with blond hair and a thin nose came over, and
Mike said:

"Meet Captain Martin in charge of defense here. He's the
Brass Hat of the digging here, too, and a slave driver with
an Oxford accent."

Captain Martin gave me a wide grin and his emphatic
hand. He was a swell-looking fellow in army tan, neat, gay
and obviously fond of Mike. Like all British officers he had
the fault of looking too much the military expert.

"Pleased to know you. A bit of a crazy chap, your friend
Mike. I hear you are inspecting our defenses."

"When I find them."

"To be sure. Mike *can* get tin out of the old earth. Say that for the fellow. Where is Fran?"

Mike said, with a purr of contentment: "She'll be along. General Kent—our military head, Old Horse—is picking her up. Hello, Mrs. Martin. I want you to meet an old friend. We used to dillydally with education together."

I shook hands with Mrs. Martin. She had been too long in the tropics and looked older than the Captain. Her skin had gone a gray-white like the pulp paper in cheap magazines, and there were rings under her eyes, and I talked to her of defense, but she acted as if I had an odor—an American odor.

III

Someone had started the gramophone under the caged parakeets and it was spinning out Noel Coward's *Some Day I'll Find You*. It sounded so sad out here in the heat and the insect-filled mist among the fading women and the defenses that weren't there. I ate some blancmange and felt better; damn, I held no rubber or tin shares.

There was a flurry of excitement around the door, and a few of the ladies banged heads together for a little gossip in the suffocating air—so I knew Fran had arrived. Mike pulled at his white piqué tie and looked as happy as if someone had handed him heaven for a back yard. I could understand, as she advanced smilingly. She walked in that natural graceful strut so few women have and so many copy badly. A sort of leggy spiritual indolence. She was wearing a crayon-blue gown draped like a Greek vase painting around her wonderful figure and her red-gold hair was piled into a slim headdress caught in a jeweled knot behind one ear. Behind her walked General Kent, K.C.M.G., C.B., D.S.O.,

Retired, now barking off Jap invasion talk. He was a big beak of a man with a skin like a rare old book binding, the nose of a whiskey drinker and the long white mustache of an army martinet. "The kind of man England could use less of," Shad Roe used to say.

Mike muttered some happy introductions in a moderated voice. I held a slim small hand, then I pumped fists with the General, who said something that sounded like *"American chap, what?"* in a malicious undertone and I was afraid to ask about the defense.

Then someone started the gramophone again, and Benny Goodman suddenly made me very homesick. But there I was, dancing with Mrs. Martin and she was telling me about the ungainly piggish elephants that came and raided her flower gardens and I'm afraid I wasn't very interested and that there was a persistent stumble to my dance steps and I wondered what they were doing at this hour in Tokyo.

IV

Most everyone left nearly sober, and all the ladies had gone. It was late and we had been drinking and telling strange stories, some of them true.

The low-hanging oil lamp sucked air and smoked with a biting, acid odor. It flared up. The heat was worse—a dark night heat, highlighted by oil lamps and at the head of the ironwood table, marked with rings from careless drinks, sat General Kent, K.C.M.G., C.B. and all the rest of it. In front of him stood a small glass of whiskey, the crushed cadaver of a spider, and his sweat-wet hanky (usually carried up his sleeve).

Three mine managers, the head of the company and two Dutch strangers, stood around looking as if they had been awakened in the middle of the night and rushed into this appalling atmosphere. One boy still stood behind the bar, mixing drinks and bringing them to the ironwood table.

From the fading blackness outside the windows a pelting monsoon beat against the sere and tiger grass clearing. In the native huts weird music started up again.

Gruesomely tattooed against the coming mist of the dawn, I made out syenite crags, and then the massive creepers, the

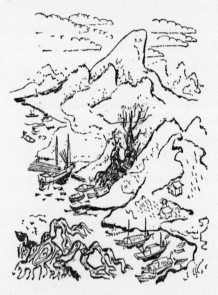

plantain groves, the maize fields. From the steep hill trails the tin mine night shift was staggering down in weary rain-washed groups.

The little fat doctor, his glasses dangling on their long ribbon, yawned. "Reminds me of whore's story in Pekin. . . ."

V

I went to the bank of windows, looked out into the opaque mist rising hot and dreadful over the inundated river lands.

"There was a neat piece in Hong Kong. . . ."

The boy put some clean glasses on the bar. The first ray of dawn broke against the glass held in my hand.

"Her mother had been in a house in Bombay."

The boy began to turn out the lamps. General Kent gave up trying to think of another sex story. We were too tired and too warm to think of one ourselves. The little doctor said: "So he married her and no white chap ever spoke to him again."

"Better be getting along. Wedding at ten, you know."

The drink fest broke up. Mike and I went over to his place and had cold water thrown over us again by the bucket.

I said: "Do all drinking binges out here take this form? Prep school bull sessions—dull ones . . . ?"

"Yes, right out of Homer."

"No . . . *not* Homeric. Homer wrote of warriors."

I got an extra bucket of water as an answer.

"That's no way for a best man to talk."

VI

It was a warm wedding. Little dark boys ran around the church with palm fronds, stirring up the insect life that mocked the screens. The groom was very warm and the bride very amused. The English vicar was suffering from some fever and the Church of England ritual was a little fluty. But it was over quickly and we opened our shirts and scratched our prickly-heated chests.

That night there was another beano at the club and in the morning I went back to Singapore. Mike has taken his bride off to the most hidden tin mine for a honeymoon.

I am afraid they think my sense of romance is warped, because I sent them a copy of *Mein Kampf* as a wedding present.

The General saw me off. He said: "Worries, old chap, about our defense are over. Just had a chit from Sing. Four hundred Australians have landed to bolster up things. . . ."

I forgot to show how overjoyed I was. (Each white was able to kill a hundred Japs—in those days. . . .)

Chapter 21

CARRY ON

Not all the anti-British stuff comes from Berlin. . . .

The little Scotsman, with the black patch over one eye, in his Major's uniform, had been showing me the big guns set around Singapore. They were very big and very much polished up and there were a lot of them and the Major was very happy to have me touch them, so I could write back how tough and ready Singapore was. The guns were set in heavy reinforced concrete—set to fire only out to sea. I turned my head around and looked back toward the jungle.

"Suppose," I asked, "mind you, I'm an unmilitary mind— but suppose . . ."

"Quite."

"Suppose you wanted to turn these guns around and fire into the jungles?"

"What for, old chap?"

"Suppose the Japs land up the coast and come in through the back yard?"

He smiled—not too much—I was a fool, *but* a guest. "The guns can't be turned around. They're set solid. No one 'walks there,' you know."

"That's what everyone except Japs tell me."

II

I stayed on in Singapore because the mood hadn't ordered me anywhere else and because I had discovered Bayes' American Bar and Grill. . . .

Bayes is a great boy. A big broth of a lad. Standing six-feet-four in his shaggy socks, and he mixes the finest dry Martini in the whole East. He also knows some grim yarns about the Trouble in Dublin during the old days of the Black and Tan, before the bigots ruined hopes of a real free Ireland and settled for the I.R.A.

He taught me Gaelic on the side. And one fine hot muggy day, it was Christmas Day, I could chatter about *Tir na Og,* which is the Country of the Young, and of *Hy Brasil* which is the Golden Land that is Ireland. And we sadly admitted Ireland had failed all the heroes who had died for her. It was now just Franco's Spain cut down, said Bayes.

I remember that Christmas because Bayes' cracked gramophone was playing the *Preizlied* of the *Meistersinger,* and because the dirtiest beachcomber I ever heard with a public-school accent came in and tried to mooch a drink. Bayes vaulted his bar with a *"Sigle nid Amhlaoible!"* (which is, I think, good Gaelic for "To hell with England!") and was about to heave the beachcomber out on his shoulder blades when I said I would buy drinks because I know how it feels to miss them.

III

He was a proper stage beachcomber, right out of *Ebb Tide* and Conrad, and his red blob of a face was framed in sun-bleached hair. Almost white hair—hay-colored, but still showing here and there its once bright red hue. He was a hulk of a man with his right arm bent and maimed and when he turned I saw a face very disfigured by a series of long scars that had torn his cheeks to a pulp and had healed into huge parallel welts. His mouth was a slim slit with hard corners. I suddenly leaned against the bar and called for a bottle of Three Star because something had clicked into place.

"Smith-Brasil, by all that's holy! You!"

The hulk nodded and passed a dirty red hand over his face. "Yes, knew you at once. You're drinking too much. Purple veins all over your face." He poured himself a gulp. "Well, bottoms up."

We had some more and I drew him over to a table and fed him and kept the bottle close and I looked into his face (that took courage) and said: "The tiger?" For fully five minutes he didn't speak. I asked again and I wanted the story very badly—even if it wasn't much of a story and a fraud, most likely.

Smith-Brasil nodded. "The tiger. But that isn't what brings me out here dragging my leash. Listen, you're a writer chap. I've got something to tell you and something I can't hold alone any more. You'll understand. You writers. Understanding chappies."

Smith-Brasil looked at me with what remained of his face and I couldn't read a thing in it. It was like a few shreds left in an old book torn apart. He looked at me and passed his fist over his face again. Then he spoke and he was again a big, dull Englishman in a strange, gaudy setting.

"That waterfall—that bridge in Ceylon—remember?"

"Yes, where your wife ran off into the river. Rotten on you, I know, but don't harp on it."

He shook his head to deny, or to clear it; I don't know which. "She didn't run off. I killed her with a shot through the middle of her forehead. Released the brake on her car and pushed it over and down on those rocks. I'm a murderer —a cold-blooded murderer. Now you know. There."

"Of course. Now tell me about the tiger."

"You've got to believe me because my wife *still* walks the earth. I *see* her! I talk to her. There was a woman in England I wanted—understand?"

"Yes."

"The woman in England was not a proper kind of woman. I went to England to marry her—after—after—and she laughed at me. So I came back to Ceylon. Remember me getting on the plane at Malta?"

"Buck up. We all think we're killers at one time or another. Shock of that tiger."

The hulk looked into his glass. "No—no shock. That night you and I got tight on the native vintage she appeared for the first time. She was just as she had always been. Polite, calm, low-voiced—*only* her white silk suit was soaked wet from the river bottoms and there was river sand in the seams, and right in the middle of her forehead there was a small bullet hole that bled slightly. Just three or four drops, and she wiped them off with her handkerchief."

"What did she say?" I've been told some tall stories by schizophrenics and manic-depressives but this poor battered barfly was telling the best story I ever heard from anyone. A tiger doesn't win often but when he does, he breaks more than bones.

He was schizoid, all right.

Smith-Brasil refilled his glass; gulped it down. "She said she was going up to your room and warn you against staying under a murderer's roof. Remember how I crashed in? Did she really warn you?"

I looked about me. Bayes had put on a new special Christmas record. A Russian Mass, *Christos Vsiokres—Christ Is Risen.* The poor bastard needed a shot of luminol. "The tiger—tell me about him."

IV

There was pity for me in the beachcomber's eyes. "You don't believe? All right. About the tiger. It was fine shooting. Fifty beaters, six elephants, good tall yellow grass. I got three beggars, all over fifteen feet from nose to vent. But she got me maimed."

"A lady tiger?"

"My wife."

"Oh. . . ."

"Yes—oh," he said, looking over his shoulder. I wondered about dementia praecox—he was pretty involved. "I was hunting it alone with an elephant and a native in some rank grasses. Good day for it, with the beaters miles out stirring things up with tin pans and spears. Suddenly my wife walked out of a clearing toward me as calmly as if she were taking a stroll around her rose garden. Neat and trim in her white silk suit, *but* sopping wet it was, and there was just a small red hole in her forehead to show how it all happened—not bleeding much. Nothing else to show she was really dead— or is she?"

I put down my glass. "Go on."

"She said she wanted to speak to me alone. So I slipped off my elephant against the shrill protest of the native. We walked into some cover. There she had the tiger waiting for me. It happened like a snap of the fingers. *Fast.*"

V

I just sat back and felt the last drink stir within me and maybe it was fear of something. The beachcomber had closed his eyes; he was breathing hard and his scarred red face, feathered with a scrubby beard, was damp with sweat. He spoke without opening his eyes.

"I don't think she wanted that tiger to kill me. That would have been too easy. I got clear of the beast after he had carried me for miles—but I've never been clear of her since. I've been everywhere, done everything—but always she finds me. She, always so trim and clean in her river-bottom wetness, with that nasty little hole in her forehead. Listen, this morning *again*. Christmas morning. Saw her again."

I signalled Bayes for the chit. "What does she want?"

"She keeps asking why I did it." The big man began to sob, blinking his pathetic eyes, and two people at the bar stopped to look at him. "She followed me in here. That's why I ducked into this place. Haven't been near a really good place for years. Clothes all wrong, I guess. Yes—my clothes —not in proper shape any more. Season's greetings. All wrong."

How like an Englishman, even a mad one, I thought. I put

down a fiver and shoved the note toward him. "Here, stay here as long as you want and come to my hotel—the Royal— tonight and I'll fix you up with some clothes."

"Thanks." He took my arm. "But if she asks for me— mum's the word."

I winked down at him and he plucked weakly at the beginning of a ragged pendant mustache, fair on his face, and I guessed he belonged behind bars but it was none of my business.

"Mum's the word. Merry Christmas!" I said, taking leave of Smith-Brasil forever. I had drunk too much in the heat and was seeing things myself. I swear it. Tables moved, I had trouble finding the door as it kept jumping out of my reach. The heat and the drink had done something to my eyes.

VI

I felt better outside in the bright noonday sun and even the dirty natives looked charming; even the brass sellers' yapping sounded like good music. Bayes had potent drink. The brass sellers were doing a small, insulting business in brass ashtrays with some white-clad customers. I pushed my way past them, and one of the women turned toward me and spoke. At first I couldn't hear her. Then it sounded small and polite in my buzzing ears.

"Pardon me. Have you seen a tall man with a scarred face pass this way?"

I didn't answer. I didn't want to cause any trouble, if she were his keeper, and so I ducked my head in the bright sunshine and went on. And then I suddenly had an idea and I turned and looked back. But the woman in white was gone. She was nowhere in sight.

VII

Well, that's all there is to it. If I had looked up and seen that the woman's white suit *was* sopping wet, and *if* she had a small red hole in the middle of her forehead, I would have had a hell of a story. But I looked up and I didn't see anything. . . .

VIII

By now the Japs are in Hong Kong, Singapore, Java. I wonder how they found out that the English never expected anyone to walk there through the jungles? Spies, most likely. . . .

JACK TAR

Every morning the sailor would come into my cabin and toss cold sea water on the cabin floor and stir it wetly with a small tired mop, and then he would remove an inch of cigarette from a small red mouth and ask: "Did you want more doin?"

"No, thank you."

"This ain't a passinger ship, you know."

"You did enough."

"We is very short-handed."

"I hope I've been no bother."

"Well, not as much as school teachers are."

"Carry a lot of school teachers?"

"Truck loads of 'em in the ole days. Not many now."

"Romantic aren't they?"

He looked at me and put his butt of tobacco on the floor and carefully killed it with a heavy heel. "I never could make them out. They used to come on board chattin' and howlin' and grinnin,' you'd think they was going to a three-

day drunk. . . . Then the sea would rise up a little and they
would go green and hold on and spill back their food. It
was dreadful."

"Did they find romance?"

"I wouldn't be knowin' . . . but the first mate says he's a
white Russian, . . . not that I *ever* called him a nigger . . . he
says there ain't no fun goin' to sea anymore. First the ole
war takes all his money and his land, he says . . . now this
one takes his school teachers. He don't like this war. Shall
I give you another bucket of water. No?"

"No."

Chapter 22

CHINA

THIS *was the land of China, and it was very big and Chico wondered how anyone could ever understand it and write of it honestly, even in that howling known as journalism. There were a hundred Chinas and a thousand kinds of Chinese, and they lived at Paoting and Changsha and Sian; and little warped men from Nippon were every place, selling a New Order of their own. That made the fifth New Order Chico*

*had seen, and he knew he would never be an expert on
China, not sitting in a mission garden among snapweed,
marguerite daisies and harebell. . . .*

THE LAND

"All right," said James Lu (who had been to Columbia
and had three wives and spoke English out of the *True
Story* magazine), "I will show you China."

A white man smiled. . . .

"China, acutely miserable, cannot be shown. No white
man like myself," said the spice merchant to me, "can ever
see it all, no reporter, or wandering 'expert' in a hurry to get
home to write a book, no lady reporter in pressed pants who
poses and photographs like a wet seal, can ever say anything
of importance about China. Not even lady novelists who
write in a style watered down from the Bible and Kipling
and Faith Baldwin at their worst, and who loves just everybody—not even they can write as experts on China. For the
Chinese are not even experts on themselves."

James Lu said, "Yes, that is true."

II

But anyone going from Hanoi (given by Vichy France to
the Japs) up through Kwangsi and to Hankow, up the
Yangtze to the plains of Szechwan, and across Shensi to the
Yellow River can find *some* things out. Not flying in big
planes—but on the earth.

There was no danger when I went, except from fever, dirt,
disease, hunger and fleas.

As yet the slant-eyed Japs hissed kindly at white men, but

the lid would be off soon, a Nippon captain with an affectation of gentility told me.

"We have plenty Rockefeller oil, plenty damn Ford trucks. We kick you out Asia, yeah, soon. You sell us a war complete to kill you with. You sell anything for money."

And of course I laughed (because I knew any American or Englishman could lick two dozen Japs before breakfast). But I did see China and what I saw is here, and there is a lot I didn't see, but I don't write of it. . . .

III

Five years ago the Japanese stirred in their rats' nests of islands and felt the call to go and take over half the world. They began with China and are there still. They laboriously may take China in the next year or so, for the Chinese are very tired. Heroism has its limits, the bodies of even Chinese women can bear only so many children, the great land of China is strangling in the grip of the Jap master, the roads to the outer worlds are being blocked, the sea coasts are gone. I know this is not the popular outlook on China. Everyone in the white race is ready to carry on until the last Chinese cadaver is tossed into a ditch. But I said I was no expert and that I could write of only what I saw.

The whole outer edge of the Chinese fabric of living is firm in the grip of the invader.

IV

But China is big (says James Lu). We shall eat. Economic chaos alone will not ruin China. Wheat grows by yellow rivers, in the hills the terrace crops are a bright aerial green. And the rice has been good for two years. . . .

I have seen these fields. Yes, there is food there. Not enough. Not a rich feast, maybe—unless you are a merchant making a good thing of the war, or connected with one of the big families around the Leader. But the food problem is not too bad.

There is a certain kind of price control and, anyway (says James Lu), we Chinese masses have never eaten much. The *stengahs* and *rystafels* for tiffin are for Dutch and American oil men.

And clothing and tools? The shops I saw were almost empty. The commodities are just not there. Price fixing helps a little. Yarns go to every family that will have them, and homespun cloth is turned over at a fixed price, and somehow it is sold at a low fixed price so you don't have to go naked. There is enough for the army and the government people and if you stand in line long enough, maybe there is enough for everyone. And you could always exercise a small wile and get stuff somehow.

V

The big money in formidable dimensions is made in smuggling medicines. The great airplanes, too few, bring in quinine from India and they need it. I have had a mild fever for three weeks. The natives can buy quinine in certain cities but they must swallow it in the shop—no taking it out for a sick friend and selling it in the black markets for lucrative trading.

Frankly, there is no Chinese Chicago industry, no factories and great mills that amount to anything. The rich Chinese mill owners that built the great factories along the sea coast have, as in all countries, gone over to the invaders to protect their dividends when things got tough. Chinese businessmen, like businessmen all the world over, don't give much of a damn about their native soil. It's dividends that count—and so the Chinese industry that is still Chinese is spindles and looms in cottages, hand forges, small oil presses and native shapers of crude objects. There is almost a total lack of electrical power. The workers are there but the machines work for other masters.

"But it was nice to see all the Baptist missions and priests and Christian altars in China," said James Lu. "It was a noble division of white man's magic; the machines, the oil, the bombs and airplanes were sold to Japan, and the missions and priests and altars were given to China." James Lu, I think, has been spoiled by Columbia; he still puts a rotary milling machine above Moses and St. Paul.

VI

James Lu has an uncle who is a banker. Give him a chew of tobacco and an Elk's tooth and he could be a banker in

Cincinnati or Los Angeles. Land taxes are heavy and are
being collected. Most of the income goes to the army, the
upkeep of roads and the political clots that have jelled
around the Leader and his Wife. The rich are richer, the poor
are poorer. It isn't all the brave posters of fighting Chinese
against a burning sky beating off a bestial enemy. China
as a national unit is no better, no worse, than any nation.

China needs everything: tools, war goods, tanks, guns,
planes, food, chemicals, medical staffs, doctors, any kind of
experts except newspaper military ones. She has nothing but
millions of honest, hungry, brave peasants, a lot of poets,
educated smiling Chinese gentlemen of an evasive amiability, generals, millions of hungry homeless kids and a feeling that somehow they may win out. How these needs are
to come to China and her hills creased like fat green bellies,
I don't know. Planes cannot bring them all in, the roads are
being corked, and the Chinese are not all Spartans at Ther-
mopylae—they need guns.

VII

War is the normal life in China. Work counts for a great
deal. The poor are poorer but they feel they are doing more
to win than any other class. They work harder, they make
what they have to. The middle class is hardest hit, as usual,
anywhere. As in Germany and England the middle class has
just waited, listened to the wrong leaders, grown deeper in
debt and been unprepared to take any intelligent place in a
changing world. Clerks and teachers are not as well off as
the peasants and the peasants are not doing too well by any
standards. The Chinese family system, as old as the rocks, is
broken. The wars have mixed and re-mixed the people, the
women feel freer from old bonds, the youths are almost all
off at the wars and the old dusty muddy soil of China

groans and keeps on producing new food, new Chinese, new ideas and vicarious suffering.

Fuel, food are high, rent is high in the broken cities, and people rub their rags together and eat together and eat out a great deal of the time. There is a mixture of odors and fleas and bodies and a freedom in some places of the old

ideas of class and wealth and godhood. Life is desolate and sterile or deadly and exciting. But bankers do well. . . .

I found nothing to do in China in the way of amusements (that is, in case I wanted to be amused).

I had a fever most of the time. I was dirty, hungry most of the time. But the city Chinese who are used to all that had little to do. There are sing-song girls for the officers, and army followers, of a sort, for the soldiers, and wine is rare, shoes and rickshas cost a lot of money, and city rents are very high. The bombs fall and the dead are carted away and new people rebuild the bricks into a new shape and the rent goes up. A lot of people move to the country and radio and Hong Kong haircuts and American advertising signs are replacing little clay gods in the fields. And there is a truculent resentment against that, too, says James Lu. . . .

WHAT IS TO BE?

Sitting in a lousy, bug-rich inn on a mud floor drinking black tea, James Lu and his cousin (James is related to a million Chinese), a truck driver, we talked of China that was to be.

Truck Driver spit out the hull of a sunflower seed. He had been to mission schools and he could take a Buick motor apart. He could read English and was a subtle, felicitous critic of the white races.

"See," he said, "the educated, the city people—they all time say, of sure, China will win."

"And?" I asked.

"But for you I tell you this. They much are impressed by the Nips. The way Nips have planned everything, the way they keep on fighting us after five years' losses. England, America is far damn away and the Nips they here all around us and Singapore, Hong Kong, the Java Sea lands, they are weak damn. I have been there sometimes. The Nips can take them while the Bible folk (white people) get drunk, fornicate with half breeds, and steal out all tin and rubber and oil."

"You think the Nips are that good?"

"I who should damn not admit it, say yes—so."

I said: "Any American can lick two dozen Japs."

II

James Lu looked at his cousin and they politely went back to eating sunflower seeds, noses dilated with scorn.

Truck Driver said at last: "The coolie, he no fool. He is wondering how long we hear of your big planes and great guns' voices and why we never see enough of them. Soon the Nips make war on you and then the coolie will feel less and less that you Bible people are anything but big liars."

"Don't worry," I said.

"Why not? Nips take all island lands soon. Then they try to take Siberia. Gandhi in India—he work for Japs now. For colored peoples of the world."

"Oh, no," I said, "Gandhi is a noble soul."

Truck Driver looked at me with a strong, inflexible mouth. "Gandhi just one big politico. Want lots of glory, wants India free. 'Soul' is Bible talk. Gandhi very cunning devil. He not humble, he not simple soul. That is all for effect to impress Hindu masses. He dream all time of glory, personal glory, India glory—all else just big act."

"I never knew that," I said.

"I meet many Chinese who visit Gandhi. They say they find there all big fat Hindu cotton factory owners, many big, rich India people, they support Gandhi so that when Nips come their factory and mills safe because Gandhi no let Hindus fight. Like rich Chinese in Shanghai and Canton, rich Hindus want no war with Nips."

"What is China planning to do?" I asked.

"Wait, fight, die, wait, fight, die. . . ."

"And then?"

"Maybe two years, ten years—no more fight left. No more Chinese boys to die left. Then we just wait."

"You mean, make a peace with Japan?"

"Nobody know how it turn out. We see . . . those of us who live."

"But China has large armies."

"Larger armies dead. More large armies die. Soon no more armies. Supplies very small and no place can we take field—

full armed—and make big counterattack. We suffer, suffer big and keep on . . . but suffering not enough to win."

"England and America will never let China down," I said proudly.

"English, Dutch, still fighting Queen Victoria wars. America very fine, young, new—but far away and sleeping. You wake up soon—very soon—but how soon you help?"

"America will help."

"Better help soon. Suppose Nips say to us—we make peace. You colored people like us. They say, we take Nip troops away from every place south of Great Wall. *Maybe* we no take peace offer—but it break lot of Chinese hearts to turn it down after five years' bleeding. You all have too much this complacency about Chinese and Russians. You think we can die in millions to save you, and we can go on dying. *Then* you Bible people watch out. *You* die then. . . ."

"You have done well so far," I said.

"Some time come, time when no can do so well any more. Must have big help, real help. No speeches, no good-sounding advice. We *not* all brave, not all willing to die, we not all want to see children in army and die, die; and we not all stay and see city and city go away in bomb burnings, we not all time marching and dying saying, oh, yes, Great Leader, just let us die for you and charming wife and the help coming some day. No, no. China soil it stay, and we no want to die anymore. I tell you this—you understand that we flesh and blood and bones and we get tired. We want to live."

"Yes, we all want life. . . ."

III

And that's what I heard all over China. I set it down here, not the expert, mind you, not the pretty lady reporter seeing China from an air liner and posing with the Leader and his Wife. This isn't a book written by a lug in a hurry to meet the demands of a new publishing season. What I saw, what I heard, is here. How true, how good, how full of any facts it is, I don't know. You may find a few voices that are a little different from the people you have seen on brave Chinese posters, willing to die for a great nation, eternal in its fight for freedom. All that sounds good. I love goodness, too. But a nation is the little people—a lot of them—and the little people of China are tired. Give them more than noble words. (I was shocked to find a Chinaman loved life as much as I did.)

IV

And in the morning the village burns black and chrome-yellow, and far off there is gunfire, big Jap guns blasting and the Chinese boys go past, barefooted, an old Remington to every three boys.

I am sick of some unknown fever. . . .

FEVER

This is how Chico died . . . and almost stayed dead. One day, near a mud city and an American colony of prayer— folk who ran a hospital—he fell down and could not get on his feet. . . .

II

Then there was sun and sometimes ice on his hot skin and great shadows hovered over and once, after an era of colliding, falling, he felt hands—light, teasing spirit hands that probed his organs and reached the cunning nerve buds buried deep in his brain pan, and throbbed under the skull ringing with the clangor of great bells. And forever that soft, tenuous light—but no sight, and he was sorry dimly for a lot of lousy things done—and undone. . . .

III

The heat grew and he knew he was wet and knew he was back in his mother's body and then he protested much but could not stop his birth from the mellow warmness of the womb and all around a great whiteness lay and there he was, alive newborn, refreshed, mind darting in the milky mist and fingers clutching, twisting, holding on to something. And he smelled it. Cold and intolerable, smelled reality and thought that now the end would come fast—or hope. . . . He smelled. . . .

Smelled life, the odor of things, the groping scent of bed linen and alcohol and the bitter brine of his skin, and China smelled and the wars and he smelled the thing: *man, the air of open window, the brittle darting sun, the silent odor of four walls, the gag of food and then, one time, the clear burn of oxygen, pure, harsh, biting. Without passion, rancor, heroics, Chico came alive. . . .*

And the world was still fighting. Wars still went on and he was weak as a flayed cat.

IV

Major Eliot was saying: "This is one time when we're strong enough to stay out of war. It's nonsense to worry about our getting in."

THE JAP

The Jap Army is better than it looks. It used to meet me, this army, at railroad stations, usually a drunken captain and a few men with unshaved faces, leering—and look at my papers and smoke my cigarettes and say *Yukwai da* (such goodness). I saw it in the field, a long line of warped little shapes in brown unbuttoned uniforms and guns pulled by mangy horses; they did not look very military. But it's a pretty good army, trained on guile and treachery. It fights well, it marches well, it loots, rapes and destroys without mercy, and it can last. It has been dying, murdering, marching for five years in China and it still moves, every *hito* (man) ready to die in his tracks. . . .

II

The Jap is a hard trained veteran. Some of the men have been fighting hard for ten years to some ultimate decisive goal. That counts in war. Dirty, cunning, cruel and very very ruthless, the Jap in the field is an enemy to approach with skill and care. I adore the way the American newspapermen admit any American can lick ten of these hissing yellow monkeys, who whisper back *Kibatsu da ne* (very unlikely).

I've said it myself in my time, before I've seen them creeping over the great yellow plains, inching over the apple-green mountain chains, crossing the bogs, their supply columns raising a great dust cloud and their rape, fire and bloody degeneracies wiping out village after village from the face of the good earth. The jasmine scent and paper fans are not so lovely then. . . .

III

The Yangtze, Shansi Province has seen them and felt them, knows the Jap Army is better than it looks. And every place they burn their own dead and howl *Banzai* and get very drunk. Maybe to my Europe-trained eyes they look small, their weapons are strange, but they get places with them.

They drive a two-man tankette; two-three-ton tanks not very impressive (designed by Vickers, powered by Standard gasoline). They look like tin cans, but they are said to be building thousands of them to swing over ships and set ashore in the Philippines. Oh, yes, they expect to take the Philippines (and, as I edit these notes, they have—with their tin tanks and toy guns and *samurai* swords).

IV

Near Hsuchow and Taierchwang are seen a lot of Japanese 75 mm. guns. Steel and wooden-wheeled, but a lot of them—and also, 14-ton tanks mounting 37 mm. guns and 50 cal. machine guns (all designed by Vickers, of course, and to be used to knock Vickers stockholders out of Singapore, Hong Kong bars).

There are many Fords. And the seaports in Jap hands are busy unloading thousands of other new Ford trucks. The Japs are bad drivers, the roads are littered with wrecked trucks. But they repair them, refuel them and drive on, saying *Shikkei sembau,* such a thousand troubles . . .

In a tea house I met a drunken Major smoking Dutch East Indies cigars and drinking rice *saki* and belching and he was happy to see me.

"Me run silk house, Fifth Avenue and Twenty Street, New York, *Kaudaru* (downtown)."

"That's good. You like New York?"

"Much all time too busy to have fun. Have fun now."

"You look happy."

"You betcha happy. Have cigar. Have some *osusi* (pickled fish tripe)."

"I don't smoke cigars," I said, "or eat pickled food."

"Soon everybody in Japan smoke good rich Dutch cigars." He winked.

"You expect to take the Dutch Islands?"

"You betcha."

We sat drinking warm rice *saki*, which I didn't care for, but it was chilly outdoors and the Major was very happy to see me and I wanted to know something.

"You expect to fight the United States soon?"

"You betcha. Good place, New York to live, but we fight you all the same."

"Why?"

"Americans they think we monkeys. They think we hissing fools. They think we little damn pests. But we men. We strong men. We make much war *Umai Zo* (very well). We take our place in world."

"Why not with peace?"

"Because English, Dutch, Americans—they take everything for self and say, you damn nasty island dwarfs shut up. We want respect. We want to walk like rich men, too. Like white men, like *Yutosei* (prize winners). You see?"

"No, I don't. Why this desire for power and conquest?"

"You read 'em, maybe, Hitler-San's book?"

"A little."

"*Our* destiny to run the world—*not* his."

I smiled. "What about Hitler and his perfect *blitz* savages?"

V

The Major smiled and spilled some *saki* on the floor and refilled his cup and mine. "Me been to America and Europe. Me educated, drink *cahee* (coffee). This fool Slavic-Austrian halfbreed that Germans are fooled by—he just cat's paw for us. He break Russia for us. He kill plenty English for us. Then we smash America, smash Germans maybe too, and we take over world. We have million millions colored races of world with us as soldiers. We make cheap goods and take all markets of the world. We race of Sun Gods. We only gods here below, you betcha. Have *sukiyaki* parties all time then."

"Can you win a war like that?"

"Got best damn army. You blind to it. You get stung."

"And what will the army fight with? Swords?"

"Got big steel plants on Kyushu Islands. Rolling mills at Aksada. English, American engineers they do anything for money for us. Germans build us Fuji Denki dynamo plants. You white people you sell soul for clink of cash, C.O.D., O.K. baby."

"Those are just the money-mad ones. We have others."

"We have soon, chrome and nickel from Philippines, iron ore, too. Oil and bauxite from East Indies, rubber from Singapore and Malay. We no longer be *bimbo kuge* (pauper gents). We soon have everything. We know where everything is."

"You seem to."

"Me travel in silk business all over world, long time. Me open office here, here, *here*. Me find out everything, thank you."

VI

He was pretty drunk and had an ugly look on his happy face. Maybe he was only a superficial symbol of a race—but he was mean and very real.

"What about war materials?"

"Plenty American scrap iron for ten years' war on hand. Plenty Standard Oil, plenty Ford trucks, Vickers guns and we smart, damn smart people. We copy Douglas planes you sell us, we copy German guns, we copy U.S. Steel rolling mill process and lathes and drills you sell us. And we eat nothing. Little rice, *hamaguri-meshi,* little fish and sauce and pickles and we fight. Oh, you bet we fight you Americans. And soon, soon—sooner than you think, *thank you very much!*" And he fell asleep on his mats, balanced on his twitching haunches, and I went away very quickly.

HOW TO MEASURE AN ENEMY

I went away from China sure that war would come soon to American shores, and I found few who would listen to me. The American missionaries (like all missionaries I found) didn't care very much about anything that happened outside their courtyards. Christians—not Christianity—interested them. The priests were only interested in orders from Rome and the price of rice, and the businessmen would drink gin slings at the bars and curse the yellow bar boy and remember when a white man could live like a king on ten dollars Mex a month and some plausible dishonesty.

II

The Japs smiled on us those days, great big toothy smiles, and went their way chattering that Jap tongue and writing that Jap picture writing that is so confusing to everyone not a Jap; "*Yuku hoga ii* (better take it on the lam)," they said.

The Jap started life with nothing—an oil man told me—a

naked island people living a locked-away life with low standards. They only got a written language in the fifth century from the civilized Chinese. They also took on Chinese art, writing forms and a slight human quality that never got beyond *Itadakimasu* (Thanks very much).

No means *yes* and *yes* means *no* in Japanese. English has drifted in and *horse dovers* you will be happy to hear are bits of fish eggs and chopped spiced meats. Beer is *biru* and

Japanese beer is as bad as it sounds. Johnny Walker Whiskey and Dunhill pipes (all made in Japan) are on sale in the bigger cities. *Daddy-San* is a proper way for a child to address his father. There is no real Jap word, *Papa*. O.K. and all right is *orai* in Nippon and *steki* means swell, for some reason—although none is a Jap word. Jap singers even try out *La donna è mobile.*

III

The schools teach the strange idea that in 660 B.C. the Sun was with child, and sent the child, the Emperor Jimmu, down to run a new master race.

The Japs, a professor told me, are a mixture of lower forms of tribal mankind, having run out the hairy Ainus, and interbred with invading Mongolians and Malayans. The state religion is *Shinto,* which is nothing but the full worship of the islands of Japan, the holy droopy Mikado and all his forefathers that make up the moth-eaten fabric of their herd society.

The Chinese have their own version of Japanese beginnings. A shipload of men and women were wrecked, they say, on the island of Japan, and intermarried with the monkeys who lived there; and that's how Japanese were born. In 1900 the Dowager Empress of China still called the Japs *monkey people* in official court circles.

But behind all this legend and ridicule stands a huge, cruel, cunning nation of killers, armed and ready to seize most of the world and willing to murder millions to do it. They have the confidence of all egotistical misfits.

And as war drew near between us and them, Major Eliot, "world's greatest military expert," could still find time to say this:

Japan is in no case to fight a war with a group of major opponents. Her army is sadly out of date, having not one fully armored division, and being short of tanks, armored cars, anti-tank and anti-aircraft artillery, modern engineering equipment and modern communication devices . . . As for Japanese air power, it is almost non-existent. . . .

SHADOWS

"Did you read the newspaper expert this morning?" asked the hotel clerk.

"No . . . I was busy."

"How do them guys do it? They know everything."

"They certainly sound as if they do."

"They know more than the generals."

"So it seems."

"I'd like to see them running the war."

"It would be interesting."

The clerk nodded. "Them babies have ideas."

The almost non-existent Jap air power passed overhead . . . a hundred bombers going to remove a few Chinese villages.

Chapter 23

CHINESE RIVER

IN THOSE days you could still go by river boat from Lake
Tungting to Canton by way of the Siang river. I sat under
the gasoline pressure lamp. . . . The boat bumping against

little waves, James Lu a fellow man sitting in the night near
me, smoking strong tobacco, and always that little lullaby of
the drifting boat. . . . There is something of evident approval

of life, something pleasant and eternal that comes so rarely
. . . *Huck Finn* catches that, Conrad in those early stories of
the dank hot wet African rivers at night—and where else?
Nowhere that I can remember. . . . No drug, no lust, no secret desire, can give that feel of intensified living as a boat
and a night and river and old gents selling warped trees. . . .

II

Sitting under the lamp reading here and there in the
thick wonder that is Tolstoy's *War and Peace* (I would wonder who held the river's banks, Japs or Chinese?) and screwing the lamp-light a little higher, it was good to know that
if you died here everyone would wonder whatever became
of you and a lot of foolish romantic legends would grow up
about you.

It was silly thinking . . . white men were still safe then,
the Japs hated us because it hurt them so much to try and be
like us, and they wanted very much to be like us; tall, respected, rich men, not yellow warped monkey tribes, and
so they aped as much as they could and hated us more and
more.

The Chinese just bowed and held their noses, for white
men smell bad to them, and I knew now it was a mistake
coming here for the wars of men are the same the world
over. Men died in terror and wept at the idea of sudden
death, and sweated and desired life . . . just the way they did
anywhere. A lot of lies have been written of how bravely
people die. No one dies wanting to . . . even suicides push
away the gun at the last moment . . . too late.

So I read Tolstoy and thought and read on (I would have
liked a less churlish, harassed type style), I wanted never to
set foot on land again.

"God gives it to me; let man beware of touching it." Bonaparte uttered these words at his coronation. They say he was very fine as he uttered these words . . . and he repeated the same words in Italian: *"Dio mi la dona, guai a qui la tocca."*

I like that: *"God gives it to me."* Had old Rockefeller stolen that line when he said, *"God gave me my money"?* It is an interesting point. . . .

James knocks out his pipe and looks around him at the black night. He can see. He can see houses and trees and cliffs and animals mating and drinking and running. He can see the grass stir; he can tell where the water is deep; he can see anything at night; *anyway,* he says he can, and that's almost as good as if he could. It's enough to make me feel safe in the night, in the boat and in the book I'm reading.

If you only knew what these society women are, and indeed, women in general . . . Egoism, vanity, silliness, triviality in everything—that's what women are when they show themselves as they really are. Looking at them in society one fancies there is something in them, but there is nothing, nothing, nothing. . . .

A little harsh on an interesting sex of creatures. . . . But here in a boat they do not bother me and James. We live in male order. The stings of the flesh, the company of the creators of egoisms, vanities, sillinesses and trivialities are not here to torment us. The river tonight is better than formalized relations in fragrant flats with diplomatic women being cordial.

We are passing a group of lights. Behind them are houses and people sitting in warm, lighted space, reading, sleeping, tossing on hard beds, thinking of old pleasures and tomorrow's news items. Perhaps some are reading the same passage I have just finished, but, frankly, the odds are against it here.

A dog barks, two other dogs take it. . . . The low animal sound growing in volume filling the funnel of the night. Then we pass on down the river making nicking sounds, like a horse in joy, and we float on. . . . The whole river suddenly melts away, and we are running past a vast meadow of golden stars hanging loosely by invisible threads in a smooth plain, and lower down there is a ragged army of marching bush. Then this, too, passes. Deep water snarls off our bow. Drops wet me and the book. The man twists an oar around skillfully, as if he were handing out delicate irony, and again we roll on. I wipe the page. . . .

Any fool can beat the Germans. From the very beginning of the world everyone has beaten the Germans. And they've never beaten anyone. They only conquer each other.

III

In the end I suppose no one *ever* beats anyone. . . . We do just conquer each other. Very true and very easy to accept in the middle of a river far from the Hun hordes, far from the Russian woods, the white ghost plains and bogs of the German borders. Writers are such fools at times. Their best remarks are peddled at parties by insignificant people. They write something well, they say something with a good turn of words and a thousand foolish people like myself accept it. In America the primitive mystic writers, the realists writing of farm hands and valleys and horses and fruit workers, they, too, are writing such stuff—about free people, always winning because they want freedom. Thinking free is being free.

It isn't true; it's just best-seller bait. Yet even the great Tolstoy will write of Germans only conquering each other. In the long view it is true, but we fruit flies *can't* have a long view. We shall be dead soon enough, and to hell with a long view when I am ashes under a super-highway, or a dust beam in the eye of a general fighting the Tenth World War. . . .

Suddenly the night is full of danger. There are rocks, washouts, old tree stumps like the turrets of a nunnery, but I am afraid to talk to James about it. He must never think that I am a soft, frightened man. We have lost the stars, and the moon is gone too, and in pure India ink we glide, blindfolded, on and on, limited suddenly to negative qualities. The book is still open under the dim lamp . . .

We are plunged in slumber, we are the children of dust and ashes, until we love . . . but love and you are a god, you are pure, as on the first day of creation . . .

The night is almost gone. Far away the first ribbons of dawn are beginning to flutter coldly in the onrush of coming morning. I am suddenly cold. I wrap a blanket around myself and, sitting in the bobbing boat, hurry to meet the day—the *everyday*—the *always-day*—that every man wakes to.

I wondered if any book could ever catch the full pattern of living and fit itself always to the mood of the reader when he wanted it. Of course not, for the reader is funny when you, the writer, are as sad as a colic after a low-life wedding. He is full of poetry that he can't fill with words when you are lowdown and comic, and when the writer sits himself down to write those deep, wonderful facts that after a few thousand years no one else has discovered as the great cure-all for the world problems, then the reader lets down his braces, and opens the first two buttons of his pants, takes off his shoes and reaches for a detective story—his substitute for a dull life, a dull house, a sad existence, a torpid body and limping mind.

Only in murder, in fresh blood, in sudden death cheaply done and quickly told does he find escape. He does not turn to art, to music, to the fullnesses of himself and all the wonders of recorded living but to that which the Greeks held as of great tragedy: the taking in cold blood of human life. In other words: who murdered Sir Stafford Gonz in his library, the doors locked from inside, the windows barred and the key *still* in the lock?

Better Tolstoy:

At two o'clock in the night of the 13th of June, the Tsar sent for Balashov and, reading him a letter to Napoleon, commanded him to go in person and give the letter to the French Emperor. As he dismissed Balashov, he repeated to him his declaration that he would never make peace as long as a single enemy under arms remained on Russian soil, and told him to be sure to repeat those words to Napoleon. . . .

Why read? It hits too close to home. The pleasure of reading lies in the fact that the events and things told of can no longer affect the house you live in, the health of your children, the well-being of your wife. There is no pleasure in reading that history repeats itself, it only leaves the bitter taste of asking, *how* far does it repeat iself? The full cycle is rare—the beginnings of many cycles are all around us.

James lies down on the floor boards and grunts himself asleep. The boat runs on blind but sure, the wind follows and runs ahead and comes rushing back to see what is holding us up. I hide the book in a blanket and think of hot coffee.

Later, James asks, "You like read?"

"I guess so."

"Plenty headache in reading. Better whiskey."

"That aches a head too."

"You betcha sweet life. But it easy."

"You mean to drink?"

"Sure. Open mouth, let drop likker."

Maybe the printing press was a lot of bother, more bother than it was worth. This calls for deep thinking. I haven't the time.

THE LATE HOUSE GUARD OF THE TZAR

Speed, that's what we used to call him, and all his friends called him Speed. He was a White Russian, you see, and no one who had not read Tolstoy—even in French—could say his name. Speed was a painter . . . a very good one, I thought, but of course not very popular as he painted things with taste, good color and fine draftsmanship. He didn't invent a phony school or wear raw lambchops on his head walking down Fifth . . . so he wasn't very popular with the smart people who know nothing but what is the rage. This happened in Shanghai . . . which had an art market then. . . .

Of course Speed was rare stuff. Lots of people can't believe there are people like him, and I once put him into a work of fiction and had to take him out as the publisher's girl friend objected.

II

He came gracefully across the room and took my arm and pressed, and then bowed slightly and smiled and I knew I was licked and Speed wanted me to do something. I had known Speed for years—since my art-school days. There was the wisdom of complaisance about him and a sorcerer's glare.

Speed was about six feet tall, with a head of blond loose hair, the eyes of a Russian ikon that had come out of its frame and gotten very drunk on vodka and the minor writings of Gogol. His real name was Baron Stefan Dmitri Petrov, he was about forty-five or fifty, looked thirty, and was as strong as six ordinary men, had machine-gun bullets imbedded in his smooth chest and made a living laughing, leeching on rich Americans, and organizing lectures for authors, busted society queens and English pansies who could speak on gardens and drapes.

He looked like Doctor Faustus' Mephistopheles drawn by Peter Arno in a dark room.

Speed had read everything, listened to all music, made love to every kind of woman in marvelous ways ("I've done *everything* but kiss boys," was his boast), and never regretted the old days when he was a member of the House Guard of the Tzar and beat servants with a silver whip. His pose was the exiled White Russian of fiction—a pose that kept him happy, well fed, and full of *l'amour*. But underneath it all he was a hard, clever person with a good mind, soaked in wine, and a heart as big as the Winter Palace. *Pecca Fortiter* was his motto, and his bland dexterity never failed.

"I am going away," said Speed.

"To Singapore for the season?"

"I am going to Russia to fight and murder **Germans.**"

"The Soviets will shoot you first."

He smiled. "I hope not. I have a way of getting back. I want to be again a man, a Russian man."

"And?"

"This is our good-bye. I want you should do something."

"Yes?"

"I want we shall go again to a Turkish bath and eat little salt fish and drink something brewed from potatoes."

"You wrecked the last place we did that."

I knew I was going with him and we went and inhaled

steam and took our clothing off and went to the steam room and looked at the shapes people take when babyhood, puppy-hood leaves them.

Speed held his bag of little salted fish and his bottle and looked about him.

"A race of forked carrots, maybe the last time we shall see it before it eats its own young and its civilization. Who said man is a badly shaved ape?"

"A Russian, I bet," I said.

"The human nude, striking a fair average, is *not* a pretty thing," said Speed.

"Unless you are a cartoonist. This den of caricatures pro-duced Mutt and Jeff, I'm sure."

"In Moscow—long ago—the rubbers were all women. Big blonde goddesses who knew everything. We cadets, we used to come to the baths and let them work steam on us and beat us and slap us, and we were very young and they loved us—pink little forked carrots we were, never savoring of the ascetics—and in a way I suppose we learned about life from them. So that when we got a Duchess off alone, or brooding by herself in a garden during a fete on the Tzar's birthday, we knew what to do and how gallantly to act. Now the cinema has taken over the function of teaching the art of love to youth in back rows between Screeno—but I tell you the big women rubbers of my Russian youth were better. A breast like *klubrika*."

Speed carried his quart of some strange whiskey with a Rus-sian label and a bag of small dried and salted fish. He was already sufficiently primed.

III

We went into the hotter steam room and all hell was white around us and men sat on the tiers and steam hissed and they poured water over their flanks and we walked over them and went way up where the steam was almost red hot and we inhaled it and gasped and Speed gave me a drink and it didn't kill me, but it tried, and then we ate the little salt fish and got thirsty and so we drank some more and after a while we had a fine glow and I was sorry Speed was crying for the good old days because he got mean when he cried over his drinks.

"Ah . . . chum . . . you would have loved Russians. Feodor Dostoevski said: 'man is a pliable animal.'"

"I love that line."

"Of course. Who can hate it?—or Russia? The birch trees, the dark skies, the tall men, the blue rivers, the big fish, the wide girls—like sleeping on a featherbed. 'Love all God's creations,' said Feodor. *Nyet, nyet. . . .*"

"A great writer."

"The cold fields and the huts leaking smoke, the little orgies with gypsy dancers, the early chill on the cold spring wheat, the prancing horses dropping smoking dung, and the chilled hunters lined up across a field and the deer stirring, and the race course near Petersburg all colors and, chum, I am very hurt inside with 'the sensuous joy of magnanimity.' . . . Who said that? Turgenev."

He sucked the bottle and ate the fish and moaned like an animal in labor. His blond hair fell in his face. He looked old and tired as he had never looked before. He was not smooth or slick or handy with pretty words. He was a lonely stranger far from home and very unhappy. I took the bottle from him, and he looked at me and hugged me and kissed me the way Russians do with that deeply religious quality when they are very sad.

"I am a fool from a Russian play. I am a coward who dares go home. I want to see Russia before I die. I want to stand in Red Square and see a Russian sunset—such bad art, such a heartache. I want to die and be put under deep black Russian earth. I want to rot away and grow wheat and apple trees with the marrow of my brain, and know that I shall fertilize Russian wheat and Russian food and that I shall forever be Russia. Ah, that dim murky period when regrets come to resemble hopes."

"Give me the bottle."

"No . . . *inistranitz*. . . . Take my cross of St. George, my Order of St. Tarmar. Take all my girls with their little looks and their little coy ways. Take anything *but* this bottle. And the fish. Don't take the fish. Derzhaven says—'first chaos—then existence.' "

"The fish is all gone."

"Too bad. I want to humble myself. I want to roll in dirt. I want to beg forgiveness for being a man. I want to beg, to be whipped naked. I want to be a Russian again even if only a lousy one and a dirty one. Let me be that. *Pahzalesta, tchai*. I want my tea now."

"You are drunk and sprouting lousy Gogol."

"All Russians are lousy Gogols. You admire Chekhov like all the middle-class brains. But Gogol—with one hand on his. . . ."

A big Grik lit a cigar and went away.

"Speed, let's get dressed."

"And the other, writing that loggy prose—that's Russia, really. Classless—one mass—Russia. I feel ill."

"Come on. The bottle is empty."

Speed got up naked, wet with steam and sweat and spilled whiskey pouring down his body. He stood very tall and scratched his lean, hard belly, boisterously, then in rage.

"I know what I shall do. Let's go to that foul Russian eating place near the docks. I want to kiss the feet of the doorman and beg forgiveness for my sins."

"You're mad, Speed."

"You forget yourself," he said to me. "You scum. I am Prince Stefan Stefanovitch Dmitri Petrov. Your grandfather was a peasant, your grandmother hunted twigs in hedges to bake bread when she had it. Get out before I flog you."

"Go jump in the lake," I said, sitting down again.

"Your great-grandfather was a dirty clerk, your fore-fathers were some Magyar or Dutch pigs. You dare to talk to me! Call *me* Speed, act as if we were equals!"

Some men got off the lower seats and walked out a little scared. I was alone with Speed. I had never seen him like this. I felt sorry for him. I didn't speak to him, not wanting to give him the initiative.

He stood swaying. "But even the greatest must show they can be humble. The Tzar washes a beggar's toes. I shall find this Russian doorman. I will kiss his stinking, peeling feet. I will beg pardon of Mother Russia for my sins, for fighting against Russians, for trying to send in Englishmen and Germans, for talking against the Russian earth . . . I will . . ."

And then he lost balance, took on momentum and fell down the steps and disappeared in the steam of the lower benches. I sat awhile steaming my hurt pride, and then I got up and found Speed and dragged him into a room where there were a row of beds and I tied up his hand where he had cut it on the bottle breaking as he fell and then he slept, whistling piercingly through his nose.

I dressed and went back to the hotel . . . I took Speed's girl to dinner . . . but didn't talk about him. It was a bad evening. . . .

THE IKON'S FACE

I went shopping the next day for some prints, and it was noon when I came back to my hotel room. Speed, pale and very neat, was sitting in a chair, delicately, like a cat expecting a kick.

He was dressed with great care, full of some genuine spiritual change. His head of hair was brushed neatly, slickly back and his best cane rested on his knees. As I came in he rose weakly, stiffened, bowed and leaned on his cane with the instinctive stance of a gentleman on a spot.

I said, "Hello, Speed. How's the old head?"

His heels clicked together and there was an anatomical sadness on his face. "I am very ashamed."

"You were very high."

Pale, his face wet and his eyes popping from his sockets, the way they do in old ikons, he stood there. He looked a great deal like an ikon waiting to be kicked in the behind.

"In me lives a devil. A proud, dirty devil—a devil that ruled slaves, a devil that beat women, a devil that held bloody hands at Russian throats for a thousand years. You must understand all that. *Gospodi pomilui.*"

"Look, Speed . . ."

"I have beaten my devil and tied him down, years ago . . . but if I drink that Russian stuff and eat those little salt fish, and if I get drunk at a Turkish bath, my devil breaks out. I am ashamed. I am physically incapable of saying how ashamed."

"Let's forget it."

"I said things about your forefathers."

"They are all dead. They don't care any more."

"But you do."

"Maybe I do. But when you aren't in a steam bath, I like you."

"I am ashamed to be so erratic, inconstant," he said. "I leave tomorrow . . . then maybe Russia . . ."

We sent down for a drink each, to help get rid of our hangovers. Speed played with the preposterous melon of his bowler.

I should hate to try to put Speed into a novel again. No one would believe there could be such a person, that so many strange colors beat tumultuously on his emotions.

If he has to be shot, let the Germans do it, not the Soviets. . . .

I have his girl on my hands. It is very sad. . . .

Book Six

NO OTHER WORLD
WILL DO

Chapter 24

WAR IN AMERICA

Aɴᴅ *when Chico got to America he landed in a land at war. There was a western front from the island called Unalaska, to Valle Rondondo in Lower California, and the little yellow men were trying to hold the Aleutians and the subs were firing live shells on the Pacific beach heads. Everyone expected something. The planes and men and the army*

waited facing a great blue sea. Chico was there, was there to write of an American army, as the whole west coast played a deadly game. There was an army and they were marching toward the coast to take over the harbors. And so, while blackouts and alerts held the western American front, the armies made ready for battle with danger always at their backs . . . Main Street was at war. . . .

MARCHING TO WAR

That night strange planes were reported.

I had a pass to march with the coast troops. I got tired. It was the fourth day of marching and the sun came up like a vision out of *Genesis,* and we got out of the trucks and the rolling kitchens were waiting and we had scrambled eggs and bacon and heavy coffee and thick bread and then we beefed and belched and there was a huge barn and we went into it (among a lot of beautiful cows) and we lay down and slept while pigeons preened themselves on the rafters. I could hear milk pails filling and I thought of Spain and France and China—and this was America. . . .

II

How long we slept I don't know because we were suddenly brought back from sleep by whistles, and we came out into the glare of noon and thousands of soldiers were passing in trucks and combat cars and there were huge tanks and we lined up and someone read something saying the coast was in danger and we were on full war footing. And we felt tight in our bowels and went forward. In trucks and combat cars. Some of the men got bigger machine guns and trench mortars and someone handed out eggs that were hand-grenades. Then we came to a glen and the mud was very deep and the cars went in to their hubs and so we got out to push. We went forward. In battle array. Down steep slopes of sod like green flames.

III

I felt suddenly this was the real thing—this *was* war—and maybe the beaches were held by Japs. The little green leaves on the trees were wet in our faces and our shoes grew in size as muck gathered on them. Then it was there. Contact with the coast troops we were replacing, just ahead among red-tipped sepia beeches.

A lot of little men stood across the rise and our combat cars and trucks were all around them and we moved in with our rifles (I had a heavy cane as befitting a newspaperman) and suddenly a lot of red features faced our grinning ones and a big blond captain said he was not happy to see us.

"I'll protest being taken away from the coast for good," said the officer.

"Write to the Yale Club," said our major, who was a Harvard man himself (but who chewed tobacco and went with girls). He spit now, a brown thin stream, at the muddy feet of the captain and we began to get into our trucks and the relieved men marched down the hill and we gave them a fresh loud bird to make them feel our affectionate joy at their leaving.

The whistles blew again and as usual in the army we beefed our way down the forward part of the hill and went past a tank which had turned over crossing a gully, and the tank crew were tying up their bloody heads and one of the men sat against a tree trunk vomiting and his right arm was twisted into a nasty fracture.

So we didn't feel it was a game, a wry pleasure any more but war all right, Jesus—real stuff—and went on hiking packs higher and looking carefully at our muddy feet and watching where we stepped, for suddenly fear held us and we were all scared in our bellies at the sight of blood. No matter how many wars, you still scare. And after that we didn't sing but just slogged through pools of water and marched and wondered how we would act in the real shooting maybe just ahead.

And so thinking and so marching past pastures edged in willows, we ran into a river and split and crossed it. . . .

IV

We opened our jackets and closed our eyes and listened to the cedar birds sing and wondered, where in hell was the rolling kitchen? The mud was as sticky as sugar sauce and all kinds of trucks and cars were being put out of action. And we said dirty words (but were as sexless suddenly as arithmetic, in the excitement of war). . . .

V

We went on and came to a village held by six tanks and twenty trucks and we closed in on Main Street and attacked the general store with our dimes and dollar bills and sat along the curb drinking pop and chewing crackers and opening cans of sardines with bayonets until the Sarge cursed us for spoiling the sharp edges of war tools. Then we climbed a few roofs to see the ocean while the old village wits below sat making cracks about *damnyankees* and other stale, lachrymosely hilarious small-town gags.

PATROL

The shore lines were heavily held and patrols went out to search in the foothills for certain things. I went along to see.

Late in the afternoon, when we had cut most of the clods from our heavy shoes, our scouts came back. So we fell in and moved on and then we took a rising mountain road and

we sort of lost contact with the rest of the world. Anyway, twenty of us went along a ridge and below us came sounds of other patrols, and we crossed over the ridge and were in a mean valley of little cabins and stony fields. We looked around and picked a goat-track at random from among the jasmine-scented bushes and the flow of a limpidly pure, rare stream. At a large cabin with a stone chimney, we wound us up a bucket of cool water and we drank and then the lady with gray hair who lived in the cabin came out with a tray of corn bread piping hot and we ate it and thanked her from scalded mouths.

She was a tall, wide woman with gaps where some of her teeth should have been, but she stood very straight and she had a face you see only in old heroic paintings these days.

"Sorry, all I have to spare is corn meal—but soldiers is always welcome to it. This land seen a lot of fightin' in its time."

"I guess so," I said. "Geronimo ever come this far?"

"Don't know about him—but the last coast tribes was surrounded near here."

"You own this place?"

"Well, my man does. He's in town today trying to get seed. But the bank owns it, really; we ain't been able to make it pay. My grandpap's grandpap, he first come here for gold and the ground was good in them days and he turned farmer. But it's kinda weak now and needs them rich bags of fertile. But we just can't afford that nohow."

"Many soldiers pass here?"

"Not many—but they pass and we see planes all the time. Seems they go lost all the time."

"We're not lost."

"Never could get lost here. I growed here, been here forty-six years, girl and woman. I don't see how anyone kin get lost here. Just you follow this path two miles to the crossroad and turn left and you'll come on to a fine highway —smooth as glass, leading right to the ocean."

"Thank you. The boys would like to pay for that corn bread."

"No siree! I guess I ain't going to make money from soldiers. My grandmammy she feed plenty of boys when she didn't have no too much food herself."

I stood up and held out two dollars. "It's like this—you

see, these men are under orders. They can't take anything for nothing. They have to refuse it. Now they've eaten all that corn bread and can't refuse it—you understand."

She smiled and said nothing and I felt some feversome rhythm of existence in her that the men in her family had missed.

"They'll get in trouble if they don't pay for it."

She took the money and nodded. "You're a mighty slick talker. Talk the tail feathers off a blue jay. I'll take it."

"Thanks."

II

I liked that woman. She had spirit that was lacking in the civilian part of some nations—a defiant delicacy—an ingenious courage. She was rare, and I hoped a lot of people would become like her.

III

Her directions were all right, too. I guess she never *was* lost in her life. We got to the shore. The grinning villagers looked at us and treated us to pop and later a big staff car with two stars on it came bouncing up the highway and stopped, and a General (like a Peter Arno drawing) too full of *l'heure du cocktail* got out and looked at us.

"Damn dirty looking bunch of soldiers. Button those jackets. Face me. Stand up there. Put away that soda bottle. Well, what have you to say for yourself?"

We stood very still. "Patrol coming in."

Peter Arno's man laughed. "All right. Dismissed! Hot day, all right!"

And the big car with the two stars on it went on and we sat down and finished our pop.

That afternoon an enemy sub fired twenty shells ten miles up the coast ... and Sarge gave everyone some extra drill. ...

BEEF SESSION

Sitting among a hoarse murmur of small talk in a beer-and-juke joint back of a general store with a half dozen army men and drinking the local beer, the talk ran suddenly very big about how well the local love affairs were going. Sarge was drinking his ale without much talk, but the other soldiers were telling of their great charm among women.

The mist had let up but the fields were soggy, and all around us on highways and in pine forests and even in swamps full of quicksand the patrols were still out.

There were armored divisions, too, and the muddy river had been crossed. Pursuit planes and A-20-A bombers were also acting over us, and even Navy dive bombers were strafing our ocean.

II

The men had come through the marching and patrols well. Hunger, damp, mud and muck and chiggers had not hurt them much, and they still swore new oaths and tied up old scratches with indistinct murmurs. Dimout orders were going into effect.

Personal carriers, bantam cars, jeeps, jerks, jeeks, tractors and big Macks were all around us. The planes did a lot of flying and there were a lot of them and we liked the airmen, exuberant and careless with local virgins.

A lot of low hidden cow pastures were marked off as plane fields and a lot of soldiers stuck tree branches into their belts and cut boughs to cover hidden planes, successful if we could read properly the ludicrous joy of the camouflage officers.

III

I rode in a rubber assault boat across a flood-high river and, frankly, they are not as safe as a parlor sofa and a small-boned blonde. Each rubber bath mat held eleven men, and that is eleven men too many for safety, but we got three thousand men across the river in them, so safety is not too important. No one fell out of a boat, anyway, on that trip except a *Saturday Evening Post* man. He blamed the New Deal.

There were some casualties. Some lucky hillbilly had an emergency appendectomy performed in the field and he recovered to make medical history. The field evacuation hospitals moved about a score of men a day. Most were fractured knees, strained backs, food poisoning and being socked on the head by a wheel while wrestling with a flat tire. I was interested in the men and how war affected them. And of them, what I saw I liked. They were earnest. They had beauty. They were young and they could fight and march and beef. That is the best sign in any army when the soldiers take off their shoes and beef about their food, their leaves, their officers, their parades, their broads, bowels and their pay.

In the great French smash-up in 1940, when the French Army melted away and never fought a real honest battle, the thing that depressed me most was the fact that the French soldiers did not beef.

They lacked the spirit to beef. They just kept falling back, scowling, numb, cursing but not beefing—and tired. Their officers had run away; their generals were traitors; and the poor French rank and file, sold out, deserted, betrayed on every side by Pétain, Laval, Weygand and Gamelin, just forgot how to beef naturally and sweetly.

IV

Americans beef well; it is a hot, voluptuous art. It is a pleasure to hear them. A radio report came in on some minor action. The men put down their beer cans and Sarge said two words.

"The cruds!"

"Why, we murdered de bums!"

"How do you like *them* apples?"

And it took two more rounds of beer to get the boys to quiet down.

I felt sorry to leave, but I was a tired man. I had marched with these kids for five days and eaten their slum and cursed the mud and heat with them and now I was ready for a breakdown. My stomach had given in to negative thinking.

I got up and bought a new round and put on my old hat and my dirty raincoat.

That night the whole coast stood by for a general alarm.

The beaches were manned, the guns alert and the barrage balloons sent up to haunt the sky. Just before dawn, I heard firing. . . .

NEWS ITEM

And just this morning there was a press story in the newspaper from Washington, sent out by the respectable Associated Press.

STANDARD OIL CARTEL WITH GERMANS BARRED AMERICAN SYNTHETIC PRODUCTION, ARNOLD TESTIFIES

WASHINGTON, March 26. (AP)—Thurman Arnold declared today that the Standard Oil Co. had "frustrated the creation of an American synthetic rubber industry" by turning improved manufacturing processes over to German interests while at the same time withholding them from American firms.

Such a costly wartime paradox caused Chairman Truman (D.), Mo., to exclaim, *"I think this approaches treason."*

Arnold, Assistant Attorney General in charge of the Anti-Trust Division, told the Senate Defense Investigating Committee that cartel arrangements between Standard Oil and the I.G. Farben Trust of Germany were "the principal cause of our present shortage of synthetic rubber."

"There is," he declared, "essentially no difference between what the Standard Oil has done in this case and what other companies did in restricting the production of magnesium, aluminum, tungsten, carbide, drugs, dyestuffs and a variety of other critical materials for the war."

Arnold said that an agreement on exchange of patents and division of world markets was entered into between Standard Oil and I.G. Farben and revised in September of 1939, after which it was adhered to by the American company even though the Germans did *not* reciprocate.

NAZIS KEPT SECRETS

"At the direction of the German interests," Arnold testified, "Standard Oil *refused* to license independent producers in the United States for the production of synthetic rubber."

Fines imposed on the American companies and three of the seven officers, all of whom pleaded *nolo contendere* to the joint criminal charges of the actions, totalled $50,000.

A lawyer I know told me that pleading *nolo contendere* to criminal charges of this sort is legal dog Latin that could be translated as saying: *"You caught us with our pants down."*

PART OF A LETTER FOUND IN A COPY OF *TOM SAWYER*

"It's good to be back in the States and the hospital is very good and the nurses look good enough to eat. You don't have to worry about me having my right leg cut off . . . I've got another. . . . It wasn't very much and it happened very fast. We were there three days and it rained all the time and then we fell back only they hit a lot of us. The food gave out and the top sarge went wacky with chigger bites and a cut on the head and there were six of us left. I can't say we were very brave or very scared either. But when they found us it was three days later, and Chet—you know Chet White—he was naked and hitting trees with big rocks and

I was daffy enough to begin singing and when they told me the leg was gone I just sang some more and the nurse kissed me and I fell asleep. This morning we had X-rays and I talked and sometimes I think they'll let me go back there . . . but that isn't so. . . ."

Chapter 25

A WRITER REMEMBERS
CHICAGO

S<small>LEEP</small> is gone. I go walking; walking cross town, the night people coming along with their night tools in a strange city I know nothing of; a city busy with war grains and pigs. . . .

The charwomen were gathering in a Bacchic Rout like baggy dirty crows. Somewhere they had spent a day of slovenly decay and now in dragging skirts, hanging hair (and with reeking breath) they clanked their pails against bruised knees and shouldered their mops. An army of witches, ready to prepare the temples of business for tomorrow's battles. The grain and steer markets are higher than a kite. . . .

Mad Maggie (I sketched her for a dime) stood dribbling over a huge, spotted apple and tossed an angry fist at the silent cattle and grain brokers' buildings while she gnawed. Her torn shoes gripped the curbstone like vultures' claws. Her voice cracked and whined and rose in pitch to the power of a curse. A shrill harangue against war prices. . . .

II

The fat, flat-footed copper who remembered Capone, passed, holding his stomach with loving care in two big hands, his night stick swinging from his arm.

Mad Maggie sputtered around her apple core, threw it from her and kicked her pail into the gutter. Her thick, bloated physiognomy broke open again.

"Hello, Maggie, you lousy troll," said the cop, taking his night stick and whacking it across her rump. "Get along with you, you broom rider, or I'll run you in for making eyes at the gentleman. Shame on ye!"

"The hounds of hell suck on your nates, Will O'Hara," yelped Mad Maggie, grabbing her mop and pail, "and may you turn black and rot dry like an old boot in an outhouse."

The policeman winked at me, made a gesture with his night stick again and the charwoman ran, falling through the door, into a building. The cop chewed his chops and rubbed his dewlaps and moved on to an all night eating joint to mooch a handout of rum, coffee and hamburgers. I saw him come out, reeking, belching, sure of himself.

III

The streets were pure silver now and the buildings were great shapes of dark drenched shadows and cunning planes. The street cleaners had passed on with their great columns of driving water. The gutters stilled and reflected the stars overhead. No one—nothing—stirred.

A pigeon on the ledge of a bank tossed in his sleep and thought of old loves and compound interest. The old tabby snored under the steps, devouring her dreams.

A rubber-tired milk wagon came clopping down the street and the milkman came out and left a pint of milk at the door of the copper brokers' building. The star Betelgeuse came out. A cold wind came timidly near, grew bolder. . . .

O'Hara passed again, smelling of coffee and rum. He eyed the milk bottle with disgust. He waved a palm to me.

"Some people will drink anything!"

I went back to the hotel.

IV

And in the morning at the rotting Dearborn station . . . a station out of General Grant that once saw Mark Twain plain, I waited for a train, and the soldiers were passing with great packs, and the tin hats of a new bowl shape bounced over their short-cut hair and wet red faces, and troop trains waited to drain Chicago of its young men and send them out to fight for these streets and lake lots and stockyard smells, thick and heavy—like old eating places, and these girls on thin legs with little bellies full of heroes for other wars; for a great spawning has taken place and the wombs of women are full of the genes of the race that must send its sons a long way to fight for its shores.

I had a cinder-smelling bed on the fast train and in the

club car a man who knew Hoover was telling the motion
picture actress, going home from a bender, that taxes were
too high, and all along the Chicago slums, that walked with
the railroad, reeking factories pounded the steel into war
shapes, and guns and tanks sat under canvas covers on all
the flat cars we passed. Two young soldiers in front of me
moved the whiskey bottle from red fist to fist and then to a
laughing red mouth and they sang a dirty song and were
very happy and very young, and the very smooth shine came
by ringing his chimes and mouthing the *last-call-for-din-*
ner. . . .

V

"Chicago is all right," said the girl sitting across from me
in the diner.

"I'm a stranger there," I said.

"You should grow up on a wheat farm then you'd know what kind of a city it is."

"I should think so."

"You don't know people wear clean clothing, have plumbing, work a few hours a day, can see a movie or read a book, or meet somebody."

"Not on a wheat farm?"

"You bet not," she said, ordering a Martini.

"Wheat is doing fine."

"War wheat. The banker, the grain dealer, the railroads . . . sure."

"And the farmer?"

"Pop will end up like after the last war. Tired as hell and nothing much to show for it."

"You going home?"

"Yes, don't laugh. I'm going home to marry the hick I went to school with. He's going into the Navy."

"I think it's very romantic."

She sipped her drink and her hard little mouth relaxed under its red lard and she looked off to the fields spinning by, and way off in space the last of Chicago smudged out like a rubbed drawing and the head waiter was explaining to the man who knew Hoover that chutney sauce was out for the war. . . .

OLD DOC MOORE

He was very popular at the Soldiers' Hospital . . .

Old Doc Moore must be near seventy-five now and he's still cutting away, working on human plumbing, cutting and curing with a pretty high percentage of successful results the ills of those who come to him. Doc is a great man—a very great man, even if no one writes success stories about him.

I have known Doc for years and I always stop off when

passing by to visit his faded, old-rose brick house, drink the
local brew, given him by farmers who have put their aching
life in his hands, and always remember to bring him something when they hit town. Doc has been a drunkard for
years, a skirtlifter since he was twelve to hear him tell of it,
and a general no-good citizen for as long as he has carried
a scalpel. He has no use for the new modern town hospital
and its fee-splitters and specialist frauds and he is *not* a
member of the American Medical Society and if he gets over
fifty dollars for any case, he gives half of it to his Negro
gardener.

II

Doc Moore is an old-fashioned doctor, who can take care
of anything from an ingrown toe-nail to grafting in new
glands. Until five years ago, he used to go to Vienna every
year—for women. Even doctors who don't like him admit he
is the greatest man with a scalpel they have ever seen and
that goes for press-agented doctors, too. He is busy all day
and part of the night and in between he is finishing his daily
quart of whiskey and perhaps amorously pecking at a nurse.
He also belongs to a small, brown, district hospital—almost
all free wards, with no rich board of directors or society
doctors who play bridge. Its average of babies born and
mothers saved is the highest in the state.

Doc is very interested in art and he insisted I go with him
in the afternoon and make a sketch of him tying the last
knot in a very difficult bit of human repairing he was going
to try.

I went and I saw and I marvelled. It was like one of those
cinema scenes in Hollywood and Doc was playing for the
gallery and he finished the job in ten minutes under par—
a remarkable bit of work that had two visiting Mayo doctors
holding on to their chairs with envy and I made a quick

sketch of Doc Moore tying the last knot and then I went out to the alley to smoke a cigarette. I have a foolish stomach and a set of easily frayed nerve ends. Doc liked the sketch very much and I promised to have it mounted and sent to him.

III

That night, a wind rattling loose shutters, sitting in his old faded brick house by a fire of hickory logs a farmer had brought in that afternoon, we were drinking hard cider, very cold and very tart, and chewing salt smoked ham (the kind the packing houses will never be able to cure), and old Doc Moore looked at me and smiled, his smooth brown face, his big alert eyes highlighted in the fire. He looked just the same as he had looked twenty years ago when I was a boy.

"Well, maybe next time you pass this way, you had better go right on past. I don't think I'll be here."

"In Florida?"

"In my grave. Whoever built us didn't build us to last. We are a shoddy job."

"It's the cider. Gets you mellow and once you're mellow you get morbid."

"Nope. Not me. I've been around a long time and seen a lot and it's been fun. I was lucky. From near the Civil War to the Second World War I was lucky. I was born right. A man could look around him and smell good living, good times, good whiskey, good girls. But now it's all over. The Antichrist is here—not that I'm a filler of church pews but the end of the world *is* here. Oh, maybe it will drag on— but the fun is gone, the easy life, the lazy mornings, the good ribald nights, the good food, the fine easy girls, the living in a world sane and willing to let the next fellow live. I know we brought on this trouble by not really trying to make things honest and not being really tolerant, not being

in love with all men as brothers. Maybe it's all our fault—
but *you* are going to pay for it—not us old men."

"It's not that bad, Doc. We'll get by."

"I hope so. Hell, I hate to think of anybody not having
fun—not getting drunk."

I still have that sketch of Old Doc Moore.

"Yes," said Doc, "people are dull, you have to scream at
them, jog them out of their scented rut. When I'm in a
mood like this, I feel suddenly a great sadness."

I said: "Have you ever tried prunes in warm water in the
morning?"

"Tried everything," said Doc. "Nothing helps. Yoga, raw
liver, Spengler, *systema naturae,* Gide, liquor, dames and
Walt Disney . . . still all confused."

"No?"

"Hell, just think," said Doc in a low voice I can still

hear. "Tonight men are drinking old brandy, 1865 at least. Women roll on soft silk beds smelling of bath salts and Guerlain's almond spermaceti soap. In their entrails truffles and caviar and sea moss and aspic and suckling dove and rare port mix in a rich bouillabaisse of indigestion. Vaults of diamonds are at their command, rare drugs, silks, worlds of art wait for them—Van Dyke and Sargent. Pansies have pixied their clothing, they live in places of rare delights, they travel at high speeds in comfort, their mouths are jewelsmiths' masterpieces of ceramics and gold work inlay, their wombs are sterile of spermatozoa. No grunting, like cows in labor in the spring, for them. Their lusts are artist-learned from old engravings, they never smell of the wrong things or wear out their knees—at least, not in prayer. They own the land and weep only at Charles Boyer's cinema shows or when the phone doesn't ring on time. You are as strange to them as infinitesimal calculus."

IV

The next day I saw Doc and he was smiling and smoking his cheap three-cent cigar in a fog of blue choking mist and he was trying to get into a Major's uniform left over from the last war and I said what was up? He looked at me and winked.

"I'm joining up again. The best damn military doctor that ever drove a wounded gold brick mad."

"They don't want you, Doc."

"Too old, hey?"

"Somebody has to stay home and take care of the kids."

"And hold bridge players' wrists . . . not for me. I'm going to war."

"They'll never pass you."

Doc Moore winked. "I'm going to China. The Army can't

do a thing to stop. In China they will even take horse doctors and lap dog purgers . . . which ought to empty Park Avenue offices . . . and so I'm off to the wars . . . again. Damn mankind . . . always getting their inner man shot out."

"I almost died in China, Doc . . . it's got more dirt and fevers than any place in the world."

"I'm too mean to catch anything. The germ that bites me is a damned fool. Good-bye, Chico . . . I don't think I'm coming back. I'm old, I'm fed up—up to *here* . . . just keep that drawing you made of me . . ."

And we let it go at that and Doc . . . he's in China now . . . and the local doctors are happy to see him gone. You can't get opened up any more in the town for less than three hundred dollars, in advance. Lots of new caddies around, and doctors' wives are buying mink coats . . . but Doc Moore isn't forgotten. The boys in the Soldiers' Hospital say ". . . the Chinks are lucky to have him . . ."

Chapter 26

THE AMERICAN LAND

It was the season of greenness and the colts were in grass
and the trees in green feather, and beyond the rim of sight,
as seen from the train window, the great factories were grinding out the war tools and along the railways, flashing past,
were troop trains packed with young Americans going to the
sea and going to the shore and going to cold islands and hot
islands, and I watched them pass and read a little from an
old book by T. S. Eliot that I hadn't read for a long time.

Reading on a moving train is a certain pleasure; there are
certain clicking sounds, lurching movements that keep pace
with the lines . . .

> After the torchlight red on sweaty faces
> After the frosty silence in the gardens
> After the agony in stony places
> The shouting and the crying
> Prison and palace and reverberation
> Of thunder of spring over distant mountains
> He who was living is now dead
> We who were living are now dying
> With a little patience. . . .

And there were cities below the great curve of rail line,
black cities snorting smoke below the dark curve, like a great

nigger thigh, of the right-of-way. Flames leaped from the top of deep furnaces and the flat cars went by with steel snouts of guns under new canvas. Soon we would be running across bridges and a big city would come throwing itself across the streaked window pane . . . but as yet the guns and tanks passed and the *last-call-for-dinner* went flatfooted down the red rugging to wake stomachs . . .

> White bodies naked on the low damp ground
> And bones cast in a little low dry garret,
> Rattled by the rat's foot only, year to year.
> But at my back from time to time I hear
> The sound of horns and motors,
> Which shall bring
> Sweeney to Mrs Porter in the spring.
> Oh moon that shone bright on Mrs Porter
> And on her daughter
> They wash their feet in soda water.
> *Et O ces voix d'enfants, chantant dans la coupole . . . !*

THE LONG WAY HOME

The main roads are good and the side roads better to walk on—and safer—and the hot sun warm on a thin shirt, and a lot of us seemed to think so, for the roads were full of men drifting by; pickers, bindle stiffs, barley buckers, fruit pruners, mill hands changing towns and just people on a road walking. Somehow I got thinking of a crab-flake cocktail and cold diamonds on slim fingers.

And I was thinking of a writer I had known in Hollywood, how he said he couldn't think of any stories to write any more—how his inspiration had dried up and how all those good books of his youth were all he had to offer— and if only he could get some stories—even if it meant a casual dalliance with peasants.

II

Walking the road, I thought of all that, and hell, there were a thousand stories a day in pleasant painless melancholy and joy all around me. Perhaps not motion picture epics—maybe not material my friend would find on the Strip in Hollywood, maybe not yarns he would care to write now that he gets three thousand a week (he once said to me: "I took ten weeks off to write my last book—and keerist, it cost *me* thirty thousand bucks lost pay and it only sold three hundred copies. What a percentage for thirty thousand dollars!") And I wanted to say something, but how could I explain that it was the thirty thousand dollars that bothered him, and not the fact that the book was a very bad one. And just thinking like that I came on a little story—not worth a dime really, let alone three thousand dollars a week—but I liked it. It hit me the way memorial intimacies are sometimes communicated by a look. Quickly. . . .

III

My story was a tired man of about fifty with a red scarred face sitting in a meadow heating coffee in a can, and his nose had once been broken and he wasn't a tramp—because his clothes were worn but good and they fitted him and weren't hand-me-downs. His shoes were heavy and unpolished. In the field, near-by a cow obviously with child, chewed a cud and a warm wind blew the scent of violets.

"Have some coffee?" the man asked me.

"Sure." I sat down and we drank black coffee, sugarless and it was good in the open field and all around trains passed loaded with tools of war under heavy canvas. They passed in a steady slow flow and the blowsy cow watched them pass—still chewing.

"Another war," the man shrugged his shoulders.

"Looks like it."

"You'd think the German scuds had enough in the last one."

"This one is for better reasons, they think in Germany."

"Sure. Aren't they all." He didn't talk like a hobo and he didn't seem at ease in American words—as if they were rusty. I couldn't place him at all.

"You from hereabouts?" I asked.

"My old man has a farm about a hundred miles from here. I'm going home."

"Been gone long?"

The scarred face smiled. "A long time. Since '17. 1917. Jesus, the years just went and it's '42—1942. I'm a soldier coming home—a little late, I guess. I went over in '17 . . . fought through it all . . . got smashed up a little in France, was with the Army in Germany—got discharged in '19 . . . 1919. Decided I'd see Paris and then come home."

"It was some town—Paris—then," I said, looking at the shrubbery make blue shadows.

"You said it."

"I've heard plenty of stories about it."

"All true," said the scarred man in a coarse, amiable way. "I had a hell of a two weeks—then I was broke—rolled when drunk, in a jam with a girl. Anyway, I got a job with some tourist outfit and hung around getting some cash together and then it was 1922 and well, I decided to stay. Things happened like that then. You ever read Scott Fitzgerald? I'm not much of a reader—but I've read him."

"Long time ago, wasn't it?"

"Yes. I guess nobody reads the lug any more. Anyway, his books kind of explain why I stayed. It's hard for me to put it into words. In '22 I was all set to come home but me and another American—a Swede from up the Big Muddy— we got an agency for American plumbing. All Europe liked American plumbing then, so we went into business and I said, we'll make a pile and then come home in style with diamonds and stuff. . . ."

"Didn't the plumbing business pay off?"

"Listen, in 1927 I was worth two million francs. Maybe that isn't such a lot in dollars but nobody in Europe thought it was such a small roll. Everything was fine then and a guy could have his fun and his business and get a kick out of life. But in '27—1927—my old man had a stroke and I wanted to see the farm, and my kid sister; she had married some nice hunkie and was having a kid a year, and well, I wanted to come home—before horsing around got me."

"What happened?"

"I got married. There was a Russian girl—a princess. Sure—*what* Russian girl wasn't a princess in Paris in 1927?

Anyway, she was very beautiful and had hair like honey and I liked her and I decided I'd get married and settle down with her before some fat Rumanian pimp did—and I married and it turned out all right—fine, all right.

"We had a lot of fun. Ran down to Monte for a little table play and to Nice for a little season of new-married love. Europe was all right then. For a Russian or anything else, she was all right. Then we had a kid and it died. And she died, too. Childbirth fever. Damn those French doctors. Never wash the manure off their hands. And the plumbing business went to pot. I was busted. And the Swede—he went on the coke and turned fruity. Paris was pretty low down for a while. And one morning there wasn't any Bull Market and the Americans went home and a little Magyar kid I was helping sing opera went off with a Baltic baron—a little guy that wore corsets but talked her kind of chatter—and I didn't miss her at all. And the banks said I had nothing and there I was in '30—1930—all ready to come home for good with an old raincoat and a U. S. Army uniform that didn't fit so good any more since I put on weight."

"Everybody came home in '30, didn't they?" I asked.

"Not me," said the scarred man, pouring the last of the coffee into the two tins. He sipped and bit his lips and shook his head as if there were a disturbance in his mind. "Not me. I was a little daffy about the wife and the kid gone and the upset of the business. I got a job as oiler on a ship going to China. I always wanted to see China, I said. Then I would go home by way of Portland or maybe Frisco. Things were booming in Shanghai when I got there. I knew it wouldn't last any more, but a lot of cash was running away from Europe and well they could use a plumbing expert like me in those apartment hotels they were building on the Shanghai Bund. When I think of the drunken Jap generals enjoying them now. . . . Well, anyway, I became the biggest plumbing contractor on the China coast. You couldn't flush a john from Peking to Canton without me getting my cut. In 1935 I was worth a million Mex—that's a lot in solid silver. I wasn't living high. I was smart. I was putting it out slowly where it would pay off big—in tin, and in Java rubber—and I was even investing in oil. But I knew I couldn't buck Dutch Oil and Standard. Well, *that's* all up Salt Creek now. I guess you read the papers."

"Yes. All that stuff's gone for a long while."

"I could have gotten out in time. But there was a woman —an English bitch from Hong Kong. Her husband was a big, sticky drunk who was in charge of some sort of fortifying of Singapore. You know how well he did *his* job, and he left her in Kong because the heat was too much for her in Sing. She was all right—not like my Russian or my Magyar—but for a fat man getting old, pretty all-right. I took a trip to Australia in '39 and then I said, it's just one nice jump to America and home. My old man was very old and I wanted to see him before a new stroke carried him off. I almost made it in '39—1939."

"Why didn't you? You must have seen it all coming."

He looked at me and shook his head and made a grimace of derision. "The bitch sent me a cable saying she couldn't live without me. A man is a fool, *a something fool,* like the song says. No woman really means that much to me. I was just selling out everything I had to some Chinese bankers, too. *But* I didn't—and I went back to Kong. What's the use? At first you think a woman is everything and then you aren't *so* sure, and then it's all over before you know it. I got tired of her—that's true—but by that time the Japs were down like thunder on us and I got away in a leaky stinking fish boat with a good suit, a pair of pants and a rice straw hat. Everything else is all gone. I came in on an empty oil-tanker from Port Darwin three weeks ago. Now I'm really home—

almost—1917 to 1942. It's a hell of a chunk missing from a man's life. I was just a lousy punk—twenty-six years old—when I went away. Now I'm . . . Well, let it go. . . ."

"You didn't really toss it away. You did things, had fun."

"Sure. But always I was going home, and I didn't enjoy myself as much as I should have. I was always working toward a big stake and then home. I never rooted any place. I never settled. I was just beating my way home between wars. Well, I'm home to stay now. This war isn't any of my affair. A man only has one good war in him. I'm an old man. I'm tired as hell."

IV

We sat in the meadow and we saw the corn and the widening cow and the far tight-stretched sky of blue, and we just sat, too pleased with the fine day to go on for a while. And the scarred man who was a long time coming home, the soldier who went away to fight for some principle given him by a college professor with long teeth who made a bad peace and lost a lot of future battles—he was home and happy, I think. And it was a story of sorts, maybe having no real beginning and no pat ending the way my friend in Hollywood likes. But it's a good story and you can meet them anywhere—just as good on any back road.

"Know what I mean," I'll most likely tell my Hollywood writer friend and he'll say: "No. I can't give up three thousand a week to walk along a dirt road talking to bums. Even Tully can't sell many hobo stories any more."

Maybe, but I liked the man with the scarred face and the way he got up at last and neatly brushed himself and his good worn suit and went away to find the farm and his old father.

Old soldiers make better stories than young ones, I think.

V

Then I went on to Washington and it was too confusing. Maybe I had been away too long, maybe that's the way they always do things in Washington. It was a huge frontier camp and everyone was very busy, and as I said . . . I had been away a little too long to put everything in its place and get an answer. All I could see was that we could win this war

if we wanted to . . . and if we didn't want to . . . well maybe we still would because there are always a lot of Americans who will fight and go on fighting for something Tom Paine and John Brown and Jefferson and Lincoln liked pretty much and made a fuss about. Americans were pretty good at making a fuss, and fussing wins battles and maybe I could help them fuss by going away and collecting my notes and drawings and show them what to fuss about and what to fuss against . . . And so I left Washington. . . .

JUKE BOX JERNT

And they no longer made love with neat grace because there was no time for it and they no longer sang the old songs or used the old poems. Sitting in a juke mill, which is not a prison workshop but a palace where black platters were tormented by coins until they sang odd ballads, I thought of Annabelle, whom I had not seen or heard of for a long time. And there was a poem that rose in my mind above the din of *Johnny Doughboy Found A Rose In Ireland*.

"Toss it, Sugar," said the big Texas soldier.

"Two cokes," said the hard-faced top sarge and the thin boy cut thin red ham thinner and laid it away tenderly between white bread as clean as mss. paper, and the girl lifted her skirts and shook her spine and closed her eyes and began to dance and the juke box coughed . . .

The M P came in and everyone took his girl and went out and the thin boy cooked himself a hamburger and the music died down . . . but in the street I could hear the hundreds of heavy army shoes marching . . .

> Let us roll all our strength and all
> Our sweetness up into one ball,
> And tear our pleasures with rough strife,
> Through the iron gates of life. . . .

A FEW LETTERS

Every so often the seas and the mail services spit up a bundle of letters for me, and they collect at agents or publishers. Their envelopes take on postmarks and burst at the paper seams and when I go through them I find that all over the world the twitching progress of time is aging my friends, killing off my teachers, and often spawning new generations. I feel very old, tired. And half sad at all the hopes we had once for creation of arts and pleasures and what half-measures of fulfilment we have made, and then I throw the letters away and wait for another batch. . . .

It was good to hear from Annabelle. She was running a drive-in lunchstand in Texas and commanded a dozen car-hops in tight slacks who served food and fun to passing motorists, and the child was well and Annabelle didn't think his head was shaped like a fascist's any more, and her husband was the most important man in Paris supplying the Nazis with war tools from French factories. Annabelle was happy—or as she wrote . . . "I am as happy as a foolish woman can be, I am as sad as a happy woman can be, I am just the way I always was only older and my hair will no longer wave unless I have a machine do it. Texas is so big, and I am in love with a big steer of a man who calls me Mah Suagah and I am fighting off his honest intentions. But I may marry him in the end as my French rat has cut me free in a legal way. Take care of yourself, Chico, and don't take any wooden emotions, as you Americans say . . . as *us* Americans say. . . ."

II

There were other letters too. The Baroness I had met in Berlin was a Swiss now—living on an Alp, and was doing something shady for a living. *"C'est une affaire extrêmement grave."* A girl had to think of her old age and put something aside.

Shad Roe was dead. He had died in the wreck of a Sunderland flying boat with a lot of important names, and so of course his name had not been listed . . . but he was as dead as the most important name among the broken steel feathers of the bird.

There was a letter from him, I got it two months after I

found out about his death. A letter picked out on his little portable with his usual morsel of Latin . . .

"But why speak of Horace's *Pallida mors aequo pulsat pede pauperum tabernas, regumque turres* . . . when the dog-latin of a howling paperhanger has overrun the world, Chico, and I hear inside me the thumping of coming breakup of all my internal plumbing. I am better, I am worse since you last saw me. I carry within me a soul and a liver and I have treated them both to many a clubbing.

"There was a time when I could see ahead a world again in its proper place . . . when I hoped to hold again in hand, a glass of gin and bitters, and you at my elbow holding another . . . but the brush of something tasteless wakes me and dresses me and keeps me company, and I know I shall not last to see another fumbled peace, another ten, twenty, years of foul bastards in frock coats and silver crosses and stock exchange pants ruin the whole thing again.

"I am still in harness writing that howling journalism that some Americans now print in book form as best sellers . . . I go soon across some seas to report on war fronts about to be opened. Chico, you love people, people you call the little people; you have a warm spot in you for mankind and I wish I had too. All I have is a fear that someone made a fearful mistake and the wrong thing became great on the earth. Maybe the carrot or the lady bug or the horse (I agree with Dean Swift here) was meant to dominate and control this planet . . . and something went wrong. But I have been reading Shaw again, and he has ideas too . . . and as ideas don't bore you sometimes, I copy out some lines for you. . . .

This world sir is very clearly a place of torment and penance, a place where the fool flourishes and the good and the wise are hated and persecuted, a place where men and women torture one another in the name of love . . . where children are scourged and enslaved in the name of parental duty and education . . . where the weak in body are poisoned and mutilated in the name of healing and the weak in character are put to torture of imprisonment not for hours but for years in the name of justice . . .

In a place where the hardest toil is a welcome refuge from the horror and tedium of pleasure and where charity and good works are done only for hire to ransom the souls of the spoiler and the sybarite. Now sir there is only one place of horror and torment known to my religion . . . and that place is hell. Therefore it is plain to me that this earth of ours must be hell and that we are all here . . . to expiate crimes committed by us in a former existence. . . .

It was one of the few letters I kept. The last words I will ever hear from a man who had a certain grace and calm under pressure, a full solid core of dignity under a danger that he knew would kill his world. . . .

III

And of course there is the letter from Joe and Grace . . . only Joe doesn't write, he just tells Grace what to write because Joe has lost a right arm up to the elbow some place in the North Sea and he swam around six hours looking for it before they picked him up. And Grace writes they never found out who tied that strap around his stump before he was tossed into sea and so saved him from bleeding to death. Grace drives a lorry but will have to stop soon . . .

"We both like girls ever so much more than little boys. But we shall take what we can get. Joe is the best left-handed cook I have ever met . . . Oh darling, I'm so sad and so happy and so sure everything will be all right in the world soon . . . But at night I get so frightened and Joe can't sleep because he dreams and so we get up and make tea and think of you, Chico, and talk of how much fun the *four* of us will have some day soon . . . It must untrue to say 'This is the way the world ends...Not with a bang but a whimper....'"

IV

This is another letter. It's signed "Ned," and I don't know any Ned, but it seems to be a Ned who once read a book I

wrote and sent me a letter about it for he speaks of a letter I sent him. Now he is flying a Fortress over Europe and he wants me to know how it feels . . . Maybe I can use it in a book, he says,

"And if you can't use it, well just say this is a fan letter. There were two hundred of us Flying Fortress planes in this last hop. Maybe more. We had a fighter escort of five hundred Spitfires. Didn't need them. Ever see the coast from St. Valery down to the reefs of Les Calvados? I think you once wrote of them. We went over them at six Ac Emma, all of us. Big bastards, going fine, all the guns ready and no Jerry to stop us.

"The flak hit us over Eveux where they have big plants. Steel mills and such truck. Making tanks and stuff for Jerry. It was like a dirty rose garden. Never saw such *flak*. We came in damn low, for us . . . We mostly stay high. Got across the targets and we let rip and went away fast. It was a good go, only, about six dozen of their fighters got after us . . . Me alone. We shot at them and a shell, hot as chemical ice blew up in our faces. Got the pilot, got the helper pilot, blew an arm and ear and part of a chin off the radio man and hit me in the left leg. But I had to fly her. I did and we kept hitting them. It was very nasty stuff. Blood is so red. They got in again and we lost part of a wing. Damn big hit too, and we shot at them, and, honest, we kept sending them down like slapped bugs. But we had it bad. The two left motors spit oil and the stink of oil and blood, and maybe fear. Oh yes . . . you get scared. It's not like a newsreel. Anyway we all catted.

"The wing drag made it look bad. But we went on alone now . . . smoking, and for a minute the wheels wouldn't come down. They did. We lost three dead. Can you use this stuff? Silly isn't it?"

EPILOGUE ON TEN YEARS

THERE *were nights, after reading through old journals and pulling drawings from tattered sketchbooks, that he couldn't sleep. Somehow sleep wouldn't come and he would lie there watching nothing, and then sometimes he would hear voices . . . voices of those he had known and loved, or known and hated, or known and not given a damn about . . .*

Voices that said . . . "Listen, Chico, this is a war for the survival of the common man. This is one of those wars that means a thousand years, for them or us. It's either we murder them, or they murder us . . . and right now they are doing most of the murdering. The tribal uprisings in Germany and Japan have it all their way now . . . and we know that, and know what they want to do with us, and we must admit a lot of things and go back and kill them" . . . And still he couldn't sleep . . . and the voices were like damnfool strings on old fiddles, singing in his sleepless ears . . .

II

He heard again an English voice reading from Gibbon's The Decline And Fall Of The Roman Empire, *in a pub near the India docks. . . .*

According to the maxims of ancient war, the conqueror became the lawful master of the enemy whom he had subdued and spared; and the fruitful cause of personal slavery. . . .

Hoc enim qui faciunt leges mundi se facere juste posse contendunt. . . .

And he heard also the voice of the blond boy who went to his death with the aircraft carrier Wasp. . . .

"My old man never came back from France. I never saw him. Well, that war didn't turn out so good. But I want to have kids too, someday, and I don't want them to go off to get their heads knocked in. That's why . . . if you gotta have a reason . . . that's why I'm in this . . ."

And near dawn when the sleep burned at his eyelids, but he couldn't make it stick, he heard again his grandfather, who had been at Cold Harbor, and remembered Grant plain as day, and who was dead now more than fifteen years. But his voice was as strong as ever . . . and as angry as it used to be.

"Listen, Boy . . . what damn fool business is going on here . . . are we all a lot of tit-sucking boys, growing big bellies and talking about golf and stockmarkets, or are we Americans? Damn it, Boy, what did all my friends die for . . . why did we stink up Virginia with Union dead, and rot away like hay in a thousand corn fields? For these big mouths, for these slick mugs in clover, for this talk about bull markets and million dollar motion pictures? Boy, Boy, I don't like it . . . a lot of old sods pushing daisies don't like it. Better change it, Boy . . . Better . . . remember Jeremiah in the Bible . . ."

III

But then the voice would fade out and the false dawn was there, and he knew Gramp was mad as hell and wanted something done about it. . . . Then that other voice would come . . . the one he didn't like . . . just as his eyelids were closing and his chest felt lighter. The heavy Nazi voice he had heard so often. Heard it in Berlin, or at Lady Astor's, or in Lisbon. . . .

"You are all fools. What do you think you can do against an iron race in an iron age? Beat us? How? Humble us? How? You will not fight a total war. You will not take away the fat dividends, you will not give up the fat food, the good cars, the rich clothing. You will never unite and say, this is death for us all unless. You cannot say, 'unless we give up everything and get hard and cruel and murder Germans and Japs in the millions.' You are soft. You will pray, you will buy little bonds, you will wave the flag, you talk of the dead glory of a dead past . . . of how you fought at Yorktown, at Atlanta. But it's all behind you now. We are the young, the new ones . . . the wave of the future. You are fat and heavy with gold and rich old ways . . . you can't beat us!"

And he wanted to shout, he wanted to talk back, but he couldn't because the voices retreated before him . . . and all he had again was a sense of no sleep. . . .

It would be sun soon, and he would have to go back and finish with those journals . . . those things that had taken ten years of his life, and what he had hunted for and what he found he didn't know yet, but maybe the book would show it. This business of writing books made voices too. And he heard the slick critics who lived in a stone city between two stinking rivers, he heard their voices . . . the voices of those who had led a sheltered fine life, a fat easy life that created nothing, but that could live deep in a fat past that would never come again, and say:

". . . and if this is the sound of an American, the sound of an American is the sound of raspberries."

And with the sound of a raspberry in his mind he slept, and that day he finished his job, and the street was full of soldiers marching, and down in the harbor he could see the troop-

ships, packed like a seed pod in Indian Summer with the youth and the best that had been bred here since Jamestown. And he knew suddenly that it was going to be right ... that these red faces crowding the rails were going to make a world of their own, a nation of their own and that he, Chico, was going into middle age and he didn't matter any more, nor the fat voices of city critics and stock exchange members; and presidents of holding companies didn't matter ... He was sorry he was going to feel so out of it ... no matter what he did and how much fighting he might still do. He was very tired and he needed sleep....

IV

And he thought of the Chinese, the Russians, the Greeks and the Dutch and the English and the Mexicans and all the others, and that was a lot of people to make slaves of, a lot of folk to put in prison camps, and murder as hostages, a lot of shapes to march against, a lot of purpose and revolt stacked up ... and he knew they couldn't be beaten as easy as the "experts" sometimes said.

The great troopships were in the river now ... not even hooting their great horns and the armies on their decks were singing and he thought of his mother reading a long time ago....

Out of the north an evil shall break forth upon all the inhabitants of the land. For, lo, I will call all the families of the kingdoms of the north, saith the Lord, and they shall come....

And his mother would look at him and say, "Are you paying attention?"

"Yes," he would say, but he wasn't. Yet he can remember it very clearly, the fearful words of Jeremiah....

And they shall fight against thee, but they shall not prevail against thee; for I am with thee, saith the Lord, to deliver thee.

"Why, Ma?" he would ask, "why is the Lord doing this . . . bringing them down to fight us . . . and going to save us?"

And I will utter my judgments against them touching all their wickedness, who have forsaken me, have burned incense unto other gods, and worshipped the works of their own hands. . . .

He said he still didn't understand and his mother said he was a jughead and sent him out to play in the yard . . . among the blue-spired pickerel weed and thistle balls and the smell of balsam . . . and for ever after that the odor of fir trees was to remind him of his dead mother . . .

THE END